First Aid
For Your Dog

Here, for all dog owners and lovers, is first-hand information and advice gained from more than thirty years breeding and handling dogs. Included are chapters on nursing, invalid feeding, convalescence, inoculation and virus diseases, and poisons.

It is a truly indispensable guide for every dog owner.

General Editor: CHRISTINA FOYLE

First Aid
For Your Dog

by

MARGARET ROTHERY SHELDON

AND

BARBARA LOCKWOOD

with diagrams by
Barbara Lockwood

★★

W. & G. FOYLE LTD.
119-125 CHARING CROSS ROAD
LONDON, W.C.2

Reprinted 1972
Reprinted 1973

Printed in Great Britain by
Redwood Press Limited
Trowbridge, Wiltshire

ACKNOWLEDGEMENTS

The Authors wish to extend their grateful thanks to the Veterinary Surgeon (who wishes to remain anonymous) who contributed the chapter relating to Virus Diseases; Miss Margaret Sherson for again typing the manuscript and for allowing her Bull Terrier 'Lulu' to pose for the photograph appearing on the cover of this book; and all individuals and firms who have been so helpful in supplying information.

CONTENTS

ILLUSTRATIONS

CHAPTER ONE

HYGIENE AND THE PREVENTION OF DISEASE

Knowing One's Dog in Health and Sickness — Routine and Regular Inspection

THE GREAT danger when considering First Aid for dogs lies in delay. We have to train ourselves to know what to do immediately in an emergency so that firstly we may save our dogs from further pain and discomfort, secondly that we may obviate any injury or condition worsening before professional help arrives, and thirdly to recognise with the least possible delay any symptoms which may be the forerunners of some serious infection or epidemic.

All this is difficult and needs quite a lot of study. It is certainly easier for some people than others, as many have a natural perception while others are admittedly slow in recognising symptoms — sometimes through lack of imagination and sometimes because they do not know their own dog's habits and way of life, and thus cannot recognise that something is not quite as it should be in the first instance. Equally danger lies in imagining non-existent symptoms and thus turning oneself and one's dog into hypochondriacs! One may also imagine one has too much knowledge and thus professional aid is put off until the condition has become far more serious than it need have been. The thin red line is very slender between knowing when veterinary help is essential and knowing when the condition is quite simple and only needs intelligent and imaginative home treatment.

In this small booklet we are trying to help the novice

dog owner to recognise the earliest symptoms of illness, and then to carry out the most helpful first aid pending the arrival of the Veterinary Surgeon.

Of course, the very first maxim is to train oneself to know one's dog perfectly when he is well, to know his habits in eating, sleeping, exercising. If we can know and learn exactly how our dog reacts in his normal every day life, then any deviation should warn us immediately that something is amiss. If the dog does not clean up his food as quickly as usual, or drinks rather more than he normally does, or if he seems inclined to remain a little longer than usual in his bed, or perhaps even does not pass his motion at his usual time, then our mind should immediately be on the alert. Admittedly it may be only a very slight thing such as indigestion or perhaps a sudden twinge of rheumatism, or a tooth that is aching. But we should *know* that all is not quite right. Here again we must not panic or imagine what is not there. But if any of these slight changes show themselves, we should become watchful immediately and try to discover exactly why our dog is not quite up to the mark. If it is nothing then he will be himself again in a matter of hours, but if something more serious is on the way, by this watchfulness we will have been forewarned and thus prepared to help him and we will have lost no valuable time.

Obviously, the first consideration is prevention. And here the most important factors are cleanliness, good feeding, and psychological security. It is essential that the dog himself is kept in a clean and sanitary condition, and constant checks must be carried out to ensure that no parasites such as fleas, lice, ticks or worms are present. Such checks are not difficult and simply entail a weekly examination. Any dog who harbours such parasites is wide open to the onslaught of disease, or even if not to actual disease then to bodily discomfort, and any dog who does harbour such insects or parasites has been neglected to a certain extent by his owner and for this there is really no excuse. So at the first sign of any such pests, action should be taken and appropriate treatment is discussed later in this book. Of course, a dog can pick up fleas, lice, ticks and the like quite easily – for instance from hedgehogs, chickens, birds and other dogs. They can also pick up worms from eating rabbit dung or from the droppings of other dogs, and obviously this may not be the fault of the owner, but the responsibility for *noticing* these things must fall on the owners, and it is essential to deal with them immediately. Another cause of illness is the unwashed feeding bowl. All feeding dishes should be washed thoroughly after each meal, and all drinking bowls rinsed out and fresh water given every day. Kennel runs and patches of garden used regularly by the dog must be kept clean of droppings, particularly in hot and sunny weather. It is not too difficult to go round with a shovel and pick up the faeces every day. Any post or place where the dog habitually urinates should be sluiced down with diluted disinfectant regularly. Another point of danger is the dog's sleeping box or basket. All too often the dog is given a rug or blanket to make him comfortable, but the rug is then forgotten and seldom comes in for a good sanitary wash. Blankets, rugs and bedding should be changed once a week. If the bed is a wooden box then it should be a monthly chore to wash this out with disinfectant and dust with Sherley's 'Vamoose' or some such powder. If a basket is used, then this should be sprayed with disinfectant once a month. Perhaps the most hygienic type of bed is that made by Goddard Ltd. for it is constructed of a folding iron frame with a scrubbable canvas stretched across the base on hooks and eyelets, and the sides of the bed have washable covers which just slip on. These can be obtained from most good pet stores or direct from the makers themselves, Messrs. F. Goddard & Co. Ltd., 26, Balham Hill, London, S.W. 12. They are made in all sizes from those for a Great Dane down to the smallest Yorkie. If the dogs live in kennels, perhaps the most hygienic type of bedding is Woodwool, providing it is changed often and a sufficient amount is used for the comfort of the dog. Straw is a poor substitute for Wood-wool as it may bring in livestock and may also set up a skin irritation. Hay is certainly not desirable as this will frequently overheat the dogs' skin and cause constant scratching. There are of course the small (or sometimes not so small) dogs who sleep on or in their owner's beds. This is a matter of individual preference, but equally checks on the dog's cleanliness must be carried out. Woodwool can be obtained from Messrs. Abbotts Ltd., Gordon House, Oakleigh Road South, New Southgate, London, N.11.

Good food is another essential for the health of our dog. Like humans, the obese dog is never a hundred per cent fit, and equally the dog who never gets quite enough food, or as is most usual, only gets a very poor quality of nourishment, is not going to be well-equipped to withstand any infection that he may run into. A dog must have variety in his diet, and the quality must be good. From the point of view of variety, the meals must contain a large proportion of protein such as meat, liver, fish, heart, eggs, and also a certain amount of carbohydrates such as brown (never white) bread, cereals, or good quality dog biscuit. A word here about dog biscuit, the careful owner will always insist on biscuits in packs and will not buy loose biscuit from the sack in the pet shop or corn store, for all too often the biscuit sack is the bed for the shop cat and thus most suspect. Not a great deal of fat is good for the dog, certainly not for the stout dog, although a certain amount will help to put weight on the lean and skinny type of dog. For the good of their teeth and bones, all dogs should have a certain amount of milk to drink and large marrow bones to gnaw, as both these supply the calcium needed. Again, bones put out in the garden must be constantly checked and renewed, as they can quickly become maggoty. Vitamins must be included in the dog diet, and trace minerals are also essential. These latter are discussed further on.

The teeth and ears of our dog must also be checked regularly, as here again dirt can cause ear canker, and teeth which are not kept clean may lead to a certain amount of internal poisoning. Dogs who normally wear a beard should have their whiskers washed every day, as stale food and drink adheres to the hair, becoming smelly and attracting flies causing another source of infection. So watch those whiskers! Anal glands (see relevant paragraphs) must be attended to at regular intervals, as neglect of these can cause painful abscesses. Many dog breeders and owners favour a daily dosage of garlic, and this is strongly recommended as this is known to be one of the best internal cleansers, ridding the dog of bad breath and any suggestion of worms. They may be obtained from Messrs. Herb Royal Ltd., Bridgwater, Somerset, and cost about 5/- for fifty tablets. The dosage for the relevant size of dog is given on the tin.

So, we must watch our dog for any sign that he is acting a little differently to normal. It is safe to say that most illnesses commence with a loss of appetite, lethargy and a variation in the normal temperature. If we notice that all is not quite as usual, it is wise to take the dog's temperature. The normal temperature of a dog is 101.5°, but it can be a point or two either way with no cause for alarm, but a rise or fall must be watched and anything approaching 103° must immediately warn us of real trouble, and veterinary advice should be sought at once. If the temperature is normal (and it should be taken three times a day at four hourly intervals if there is reason to suppose the dog is unwell) and the dog *still* appears off colour after twenty-four hours, it would be advisable to have a veterinary check.

It cannot really be too strongly stressed that if we know our dog thoroughly in health, and know his pattern of life, then we shall be able to notice any trouble from the moment it commences, and thus early diagnosis and treatment will undoubtedly lead to a less severe attack and a quicker recovery, because the germs and bacteria will have had little time to get a hold on our dog.

CHAPTER TWO

THE MEDICINE CUPBOARD AND PRACTICAL NURSING

Taking Temperature and Pulse – Dosing – Emetics and Enemas

THE VETERINARY Medicine Cupboard is most important, but of course it will vary in size according to the number of dogs for which it is intended, and for what purpose the dogs are kept. If only one dog is kept as a companion, then not a great deal is needed in the way of instruments, medicines, tonics, etc. But for those owners who keep several dogs or who breed dogs or run a kennel and perhaps board dogs, then of necessity the Veterinary Cupboard must be much more comprehensive. We have listed items which we think are necessary, and also those which are useful to have in emergency, and also those which are necessary when breeding or boarding dogs, and from these items we suggest that the dog owner makes up a Veterinary Cupboard to suit his own circumstances according to the number and purpose of dogs owned.

Necessary Items Required in the Veterinary Cupboard:
    2 Clinical Thermometers, Blunt Nosed.
    1 Pair of Curved Scissors.
    Rolls of Bandages, 1 in., 2 in. and 3 in.
    Small Enamel Bowl.
    Plastic Spoon Measures.
    Small Measuring Glass.
    Temperature Charts.
    Safety-pins, Tape and Rubber Bands.
    Cotton Wool.

Lint and Gauze.
Surgical Spirit.
Sedative Tablets (Sherley's).
Veterinary Ointment (Sherley's).
Canker Powder (Sherley's).
Rhubarb Aperient Tablets (Herb Royal).
Eucryl Tooth Powder.
Tubes of Vaseline.
' Vamoose ' Insect Powder (Ashe Laboratories).
' No Scratch ' Insect Powder (Ashe Laboratories).
Lik-a-Med Laxative Cream (Sherley's).
Golden Eye Ointment.
Dettol (Disinfectant).
T.C.P. (Antiseptic).
Peroxide (10 vols).
Gammexane Powder.
Permanganate of Potash Crystals.
Disprin Tablets.
Boracic Powder and Crystals.
Bicarbonate of Soda.
Witch Hazel Lotion.
Eye Lotion (Sherley's).

*Items useful to have in an emergency, in addition to
above:*

Hypodermic Syringe and Short Needles.
Ear Forceps.
Tooth Scrapers and Scalers.
Wall Thermometer.
Glass Syringe.
Enema Syringe.
Fine-Bladed Hand Clippers.
Infra-Red Ray Lamp (approx. 150 watt.).
Garlic Tablets (Herb Royal).
Canker Lotion Capsules (Sherley's).
Ryotin Ear Treatment (Rybar Laboratories).

Liquid Paraffin.
Travel Sickness Tablets (Sherley's).
Nerve Blend Tablets (Herb Royal).
Anti-Rash Lotion (Vitacoat Ltd.).
Anthisan Cream (anti-hystamine).
'Diamond Eye Lotion' for Eyes (Vitacoat Ltd.).
Oil of Eucalyptus.
Friar's Balsam.
Skin Cure Lotion (Sherley's).
Rheumatine Tablets (Sherley's).
Amplex Dusting Powder (Ashe Laboratories).
Eczema and Mange Lotion (Sherley's).

Items Needed when Breeding dogs, in Addition to the Above:

Worm Capsules (Puppy, Adult and Tape) (Sherley's).
Johnson's Baby Powder.
Johnson's Baby Lotion.
Birth Aid Tablets (Herb Royal).
Collo-Cal-D (Crookes Laboratories).
Glycerine Suppositories (infants' and childs' sizes).
'Keepaway' or 'Amplex Tablets'.
Baby's Feeding Bottle with extra Teat and Premature Baby's Teat.
Droppers for Emergency Puppy Feeding.

Tonics and Conditioners Which Are Always Useful to Have Available:

Cytacon B.12 Tonic (Glaxo).
Sherleyvites (Sherley's).
Vetzyme Tablets (Phillips Yeast Products).
Cod Liver Oil and Halibut Liver Oil Capsules.
Vitamin E. Tablets (Bioglan Laboratories).
Energol Grains (Sherley's).
Lactol Drops (Sherley's).

Invalid Foods:
> Glucodin (Glaxo).
> Casilan (Glaxo).
> Farex (Glaxo).
> Lactol (Sherley's).
> Brands Essence.
> Honey.

When collecting up items for a Veterinary Cupboard, only medicines manufactured or prepared by well-known firms should be used, and owners must beware of using drugs and preparations primarily intended for humans unless such medicines have been approved by the Veterinary Surgeon. For instance, some preparations containing strychnine are suitable for humans as tonics, but even a small quantity would be dangerous and even lethal for a dog. Also many dogs cannot tolerate medicine containing iron, unless this is prescribed in the correct specific quantities. Also owners should be very wary of using stale capsules, tablets or liquids, and at the conclusion of any treatment it is wise to dispose of any left over medicines or tablets, and not keep them for use at a future date. This does not apply of course to the kind of items that are used regularly such as worm capsules, aperients, many tubes of ointment such as vaseline, golden eye ointment, etc., but is applicable to such drugs as the penicillin variants and the sulpha drugs. Such unwanted medicines should be flushed down the closet, and never thrown in a dustbin or on a rubbish heap where either children or dogs may pick them up. A check of the cupboard should be made every so often, and old medicines should be thrown out.

A warm coat (and also a light linen one), ear caps, dog foot caps, pieces of sheet, and pieces of blanket should be kept available for use in emergency.

It is of the utmost importance that your usual Veterinary Surgeon's address and telephone number should be fixed in a prominent position on the lid of the medicine box or door of the veterinary cupboard—and also the name, address and telephone number of a second Veterinary Surgeon who could be contacted if the regular practitioner was not available.

A very useful record is a book which should be kept available giving the medical history of the dogs, containing details of vaccinations and immunising inoculations, details of any previous treatments, the dog's temperature and pulse rates *when in good health* for comparison in any sudden illness, normal weights, and other data which might be useful in an emergency. Examples of such medical history sheets and charts appear in the appendices at the end of this booklet.

TAKING THE TEMPERATURE: A blunt nosed clinical thermometer should be used. The dog should be stood on the table (if a large dog stood squarely on the ground). The end of the thermometer should be smeared with vaseline, the tail of the dog raised, and the thermometer inserted into the rectum for about an inch, and kept there for two minutes. The dog must be firmly held to prevent him from sitting down abruptly and breaking the thermometer. The thermometer should be wiped off and the reading taken. The normal temperature of a dog is 101.5°, and in puppies is quite often 102° to 102.5°. Anything above 102.5° or below 100° should be watched as it might be the beginning of some infection. (However, a bitch who is expecting a litter of puppies within twenty-four hours may have a drop in temperature to 100° or even 99°.) The thermometer should be disinfected in Dettol and kept in its case or else in a small glass full of disinfectant fluid. Don't forget to check that the thermometer is shaken down to 95° or below *before* taking the dog's temperature.

TAKING THE PULSE: The best place to locate the pulse of a dog is in the femoral artery and this is found by placing two fingers over this artery where it crosses the thigh bone on the inside of the thigh, almost in the groin. Small dogs have a faster pulse rate than large dogs and this will be in the region of ninety beats per minute, and seventy beats for a large dog. In illness, the small dog may run a pulse up to a hundred and sixty beats a minute, and a large dog up to a hundred and twenty. A dog's pulse is not entirely regular as is a human pulse, but has an intermittent beat, but it follows a pattern in its irregularity. The pattern and normal rate of your dog in health should be known to you so that the necessary comparison can be made should he fall ill.

TAKING SAMPLES OF FAECES AND URINE: This is often a difficult business as so often the dog will not perform at the time or in the place which is convenient. However, the most likely time to be able to take samples is the early morning, as most dogs will normally relieve themselves first thing. The faeces should be collected immediately and put in a small tin or box and labelled clearly with the dog's name, the date, and the owner's name and address. Collecting a sample of urine can often be extremely difficult. The dog should be followed round and immediately he commences to pass water, a sheet of newspaper or better still a piece of polythene shaped with a dent in the centre should be placed in the best position to catch the urine. It is then a simple matter to pour the collected fluid into a small bottle. It is well nigh impossible to collect from the dog direct into the jar or bottle. Firmly cork the bottle and label as above. All such samples should be sent to the Veterinary Surgeon without delay.

DOSING (a) *With Liquids*: The dog, if small should be sat on a table, and if large sat on the ground. With the left hand, the corner of the dog's lips should be pulled outwards, making a pouch, and the medicine poured in from a spoon, and the dog's head immediately raised and his throat stroked. The liquid then trickles into his mouth and down his throat. The mouth should be kept firmly shut until all the liquid has been swallowed.

(b) *With Tablets, Pills, Capsules*: These can sometimes be given buried in a knob of meat. Several pieces must be given to the dog first so that he is not suspicious, and then the piece containing the pill may be taken by him quite unsuspectingly. Otherwise, the mouth must be opened wide and the pill placed or thrown on the back of the tongue and the dog's mouth quickly shut, and held closed until he has swallowed the pill.

(c) *Powders*: If these are tasteless they can usually be disguised in a piece of meat. Otherwise the dog's mouth must be opened and the powder shaken on to the back of the tongue.

HOLDING THE DOG FOR AN INJECTION: The dog's head and shoulders should be firmly held with the palms of the hands on either side of the dog's neck, and through his collar, which will thus prevent him from throwing up his head when the needle of the hypodermic syringe enters his skin. It is better if he can be sitting when the injection is given. The place where the needle is to be inserted should always be rubbed over with a wad of cotton wool soaked in Surgical Spirit both before the injection and immediately afterwards to ensure that the place of the incision is quite sterile.

STERILISING INSTRUMENTS: All instruments should be sterilised before carrying out any dressings etc. on dogs. To do this, the instruments should be placed in a pan or tray of cold water which covers them by more than two inches. The water should then be brought to the boil and kept boiling for five to ten minutes. The instruments should remain in the sterilised water until required, or else kept in a box in cotton wool soaked in Surgical

Spirit or Methylated Spirit. However, it is not advisable to keep hypodermic syringes or needles in spirit as even a trace of this when using some immunising vaccines will completely nullify their efficiency. Therefore the boiling treatment must be used.

Make a point of replacing every medicine, lotion, ointment, etc. as soon as finished, so that you are never caught out in an emergency. Also have all instruments, syringes, forceps, scissors etc. ready sterilised for any emergency. When one needs such things it is always in a hurry and delay will impede treatment. Another useful tip is to train your dog to accept tablets and liquids when he is well by ' dosing ' him with pieces of meat or a teaspoonful of milk, so that he does not regard dosing as a horror to be fought against when he is ill.

APPLYING A TOURNIQUET: In cases of severe bleeding of a wound on a limb, it may be necessary to apply a tourniquet. If the blood is spurting from the wound and it is a bright red, it indicates that an artery is injured in which case the tourniquet must be put on above the wound and between it and the heart. But if the blood is dark red and oozes profusely then this means that a vein is injured. In this case the tourniquet must be tied below the wound furthest from the heart. Anything will do in an emergency for a tourniquet – a handkerchief, a piece of string or rope, a belt. This should be tied round the limb, then a pencil, stick, etc. should be put in the knot and twisted until the bleeding stops. In order that the cells and tissues may not be injured by stopping the circulation, the tourniquet *must* be loosened every ten minutes for half a minute and then the pressure resumed.

USING A GLYCERINE SUPPOSITORY: Either a suppository of the size for an infant or a child (according to the size of the dog) should be used. For a very large dog, the adult size of suppository might be necessary. The dog should be held firmly and the tail lifted up. The suppository should then be squeezed gently but firmly right up into the rectum. The dog should be held in a standing position for three or four minutes. If any attempt at straining is made, a pad of cotton wool should be held firmly over the anus. The dog should then be released in the garden or somewhere else suitable and defecation will usually take place within a second or two.

GIVING AN EMETIC: An emetic is an agent which induces the dog to vomit and get rid of the contents of

FIG. 1.—An emergency muzzle for a dog using a 2 in. bandage or piece of tape. The tape is fixed round the dog's muzzle, then twisted under the chin, and tied tightly at the back of the neck.

the stomach. Particularly important in the case of poisoning. A small piece of washing soda pushed down the throat of the dog, or a dessertspoonful of salt solution (one teaspoonful of salt in a cup of water) will produce immediate vomiting.

USING AN ENEMA FOR CONSTIPATION: Usually a child's enema syringe is large enough for a dog. The enema is made up of from half to two teaspoonsful of glycerine in one ounce to four ounces of warm water (according to the size of the dog). Grease the nozzle of the syringe and insert well up into the rectum. Squeeze the mixture very slowly into the dog, withdrawing the syringe quickly, and immediately pressing a pad of cotton wool over the anus and holding it there for half a minute or so. Remove the pad, and the fluid will immediately begin to flow from the dog, bringing with it the clogging faeces. With a small dog it is best to make him lie on his side for this operation. In the case of a large dog, he should have his hind legs elevated, so that the fluid will run in the right direction.

CALLING THE VETERINARY SURGEON: It will help the Veterinary Surgeon very considerably in his diagnosis if a careful record of the symptoms and the general behaviour of the dog is kept, such as temperature readings, pulse rate, times and description of any motions passed, whether or not the dog is drinking an undue amount of water, details of any food he has eaten, whether he has a cough, or whether any pain has been noted in any particular region, and whether he has (to your knowledge) been in contact with any other sick dog within the last few days.

Veterinary Surgeons are busy people, but they will always come to the aid of a sick dog if it is necessary. But so many owners are rather inclined to call 'Wolf' and drag a Veterinary Surgeon out in the middle of the night for something which is quite trivial and not in the least urgent. The Authors have found most Veterinary Surgeons very co-operative when they know they are not being called out needlessly, and thus if a clear picture of the symptoms can be given over the phone in the first instance, this will help the Veterinary Surgeon to decide the urgency of the matter. The Authors' Veterinary Surgeons always say 'We know you don't call us out unless it is necessary and so we always come at once', which is a state of affairs much valued on both sides.

CARE OF THE DOG IN CASE OF ACCIDENT: It is strongly recommended that if you are in the habit of leaving one or more dogs in the house or kennel while out motoring for any time, that a small card should be fixed to the dash board of the car intimating that in the case of an accident, dogs are at such and such an address, and will need attention. In these days of such severe motor accidents, it is sometimes as long as twenty-four hours before victims can be identified, and by this time any livestock left at home would be in a distressed condition. It is also advisable that instructions should be noted either in a Will or by a letter stating your wishes over the disposal of your dogs in the event of your death. Also if there are several dogs to be looked after, then a sum of money should be designated to pay for their keep until the arrangements can be made. So often when owners of several dogs die suddenly, no provision is made for their dogs, and this means possible hardship to the dogs and perhaps quite heavy expense for the friends of the owner who may in the kindness of their hearts come to the dogs' rescue.

CHAPTER THREE

NURSING THE SICK DOG

Nursing – Isolation and Convalescence – Ante and Post Operational Care

THERE ARE three essentials to good nursing, (a) warmth, (b) peace, and (c) cleanliness.

Warmth, because in illness the dog needs all his reserves to combat his malady.

Peace, because his nerves need to recover from the strain of illness.

Cleanliness, because this combats infection and gives the dog comfort.

We should hesitate to say which is the most important of these three, and therefore we repeat that they are all essential. But are they always so easy to achieve?

(a) *Warmth*: In order to provide warmth it may be necessary to nurse the invalid in the busiest room in the house or kennels, namely the kitchen, because perhaps only in this room is the temperature constant during both day and night. If there are no children in the family this may be quite satisfactory because adults will remember not to bang doors and to keep their voices low. But most dogs love children and on hearing their voices will rouse up and may possibly have to be restrained, and this may not help the condition. On the other hand, the busy pet owner or breeder may feel that it is essential to keep the sick dog under their own constant supervision, and in this case where better than an isolated corner of the house or kennel kitchen? If there is not sufficient background heating this should be supplemented by the use of an infrared ray lamp hung above the dog bed, and a thermometer placed for a few minutes on the dog's back or body (not upon the floor of the bed) will give you the correct temperature, and the lamp can be raised or lowered on a chain until this is achieved. Again, the temperament of the dog must be taken into consideration when deciding on the best place in which to nurse him. If the patient is the household pet it would be unwise to cut him off from all contact with those he loves, and thereby cause him to fret. But if he is used to a kennel outside he will probably be better in his usual surroundings, providing the necessary comfort, warmth and isolation can be provided.

(b) *Peace*: A sick dog must never be left where he can be bothered by his fellows either by them actually touching him or by whining or barking outside his door. The sick puppy needs especial care and great intuition on the part of his nurse. The older dog can often make his wants known but the sick puppy is utterly in his nurse's hands. A tremendous amount towards the sick dog's recovery can be achieved by the kind, reassuring attitude of his nurse. The nurse must never show anxiety, however worried he or she may be. A quiet, gentle tone of voice is essential, and there must never be undue hurry or flurry in the sick room. It will help the patient greatly when the nurse on entering immediately speaks reassuringly to him, telling him he is a good boy and caressing him for a moment or two. This may sound a little far fetched, but dogs are very responsive to suggestion and the very fact that the nurse sounds cheerful and pleased to see him will boost his morale quite a bit. Needless to say, the sick dog must never be reprimanded for soiling his bed or making a puddle. This he cannot help when he is really ill, and his spirits must not on any account be cast down at this time. There will be plenty of time for him to regain his normally clean habits when he is over his convalescence. The sick puppy also needs a lot of cheerful reassurance, and he should have a few hygienic toys to play with unless he is too desperately ill to want them. But a knotted nylon stocking, a cotton reel or a rubber bone may just give him the needed boost to his morale when he is feeling lonely and dejected. In the interests of cleanliness, such toys should be changed often or washed in plain water.

(c) *Cleanliness*: We will divide this into three sections, (1) cleanliness of the canine patient and his immediate

Fig. 2.—A simple coat for uses in cases of pneumonia, distemper, or to keep dressings to ribs or chest in place.

surroundings, (2) cleanliness of his nurse, and (3) precautions in the nursing of infectious or virus diseases.

(1) It is important to remember that hygiene apart, a sick dog which is kept clean is more comfortable than one which is allowed to become dirty. Also if the dog is being nursed in the home, it is only fair to the rest of the family to maintain a high standard of cleanliness. In these days of disposable nappies and sanitary pads, it is easy to prevent the sick dog from becoming fouled whatever his size. If the weather is cold and the Veterinary Surgeon allows him to be taken out of doors to relieve himself, he must wear a warm coat. Not necessarily an expensive shop

affair costing a lot of money, but one roughly made from an old piece of blanket or from one of the children's coats. It is wise to line this with a piece of thin polythene such as the cleaners return over a suit or dress. This will ensure that the material of the coat will not get soiled. Be careful to see that the material of the coat does not touch the root of the tail when the dog is standing; many dogs are sensitive at this point and will sit down and refuse to relieve themselves if the coat is too long.

Bedding must be either of a disposable or washable nature. Indoors, pieces of old blanket in winter, or old sheeting in summer which can be easily replaced. Out of doors, one of the well-known brands of medicated Wood-wool will keep the dog, whether large or small, in a comfortable, warm and clean condition. If it is essential to keep the patient free from any loose bedding, Woodwool can still be used by putting it into a clean washed sack for a large kennel dog, or an old pillow-case for a small one. After an operation it will greatly add to the comfort of the dog if a piece of foam rubber easily bought at Woolworths or any furniture shop, is placed at the bottom of the bed or basket. This is, of course, unsuitable for puppies or very young dogs as they may chew it unless it is encased in very strong washable material.

The mouth, eyes, ears, anus, penis and vulva must be kept scrupulously clean. The mouth should be swabbed round with cotton wool moistened with a weak solution of cold boiled water and lemon juice, while the eyes should be washed with plain boiled water or a solution of Witch Hazel. The anus, penis or vulva should be swabbed off with slightly warm water to which has been added a small amount of a suitable disinfectant, and then the parts dried with cotton wool and a smear of vaseline applied.

(2) *Cleanliness of the Nurse*: Even when the illness is not of an infectious nature it is wise to keep a special

overall or apron to hand which can easily be slipped on when attending to the patient, and one must be firm with oneself about wearing it on all occasions. In surgical cases washing and scrubbing of hands is often more important before touching the patient than after, but the golden rule is really to wash well before *and* after. A mild disinfectant should be added to the washing water.

(3) *Cleanliness in Infectious Cases*: Here the most important part is of course complete isolation from the other dogs and in some cases from children as well. Your Veterinarian will advise on this point. Efficient isolation is not difficult to achieve if one really puts one's mind to it, remembering that no detail is too small to be of vital importance. If it is possible to place the sick dog in a kennel or room which is separated from other dogs everything is comparatively easy, but this is not always possible. The Authors once had to nurse two dogs with an acute virus disease in the centre kennel of five, in which lived eight other valuable show dogs which could not be moved, and thanks to the Veterinarian's skill and careful attention to the minutest detail of isolation and disinfectation, the disease did not spread, though only wire fences separated the five kennels. In a case like this a complete set of outer clothing including rubber boots and head scarf must be hung inside or near the kennel, also a bowl of disinfecting solution for hand washing and a tray of the same but stronger solution for stepping in. It is no use just slipping on a coat over one's other clothes, leaving slacks, shoes etc. open to germ carrying to other dogs. Wrist-watches, bangles, rings, etc. must always be removed as they can pick up and carry infection.

If the dog is being nursed in the house it is a good idea to have a towel soaked in disinfectant lying on an old tin tray outside the door. Stepping on this will not harm one's shoes and will prevent the carrying of germs over the rest of the house.

CONVALESCENCE: Having pulled our friend through his illness, our main thought must be to build up his health and nerves with great care, and to go slowly in order to prevent any possible relapse. This is more difficult with puppies and young dogs who are very liable to exhaust themselves if given the chance. The best body building foods must be given, particularly bearing in mind that those with a high protein and vitamin content would be most beneficial. One does not want to fill the convalescing dog with a lot of carbohydrates, starch and

FIG. 3.—A head bandage (not to be used in cases of canker or ear operation where the flap must not be closely bound to the ear channel).

roughage which has little feeding value and takes up valuable space. Feeding must be regular and carefully graded as the dog grows stronger.

Exercise too must be carefully watched, and short periods in the open air where the dog can fill his lungs to capacity will do him a tremendous amount of good at this stage.

In the case of a show dog, great skill is needed to bring him back into top show condition. The coat will need much attention, and will probably benefit from a restorative or tonic rubbed well into the skin. If the dog has been nursed under an infra-red ray lamp, the heat of this must be very gradually reduced by raising the lamp

B

slowly further and further away. The body penetrating warmth of such a lamp must never be suddenly switched off. If a coat has been continuously worn, this must be replaced by a thinner one, and then finally removed altogether.

Be careful when putting the convalescent dog out to relieve himself that he is not left out too long, as he may thereby run the risk of becoming chilled or over-tired. The good nurse will never forget that convalescing after a severe illness or operation must of necessity be a slow and steady process.

BEFORE AND AFTER OPERATIONS: Where anaesthesia is involved, the dog will need special attention, but so often in the case of a dog, the giving of an anaesthetic has to be carried out without much prior notice; for instance, in the case of fractures or road accidents. But where one does have time to prepare, the dog should have no solid food for twelve, or even eighteen hours beforehand. It is risky for the dog to have an anaesthetic on a full stomach, and he will certainly take sedation better if his stomach is empty. If possible, a mild aperient should be given, and for this purpose Herb Royal Rhubarb Tablets are excellent. It is essential when the surgery involved is not a real emergency, that the dog has ample opportunity to relieve himself before being taken to the Veterinary Surgeon.

There are also quite a lot of preparations to be made in readiness for his return. His bed should be completely clean, and covered with a clean rough towel or sheeting, and as he will be suffering a certain amount of shock, warmth must be provided. Hot water bottles are the best form of warmth, and should be wrapped securely in pieces of blanket, so that there is no possibility of the dog suffering any burn, and they should be placed at his back and his feet. Invalid food should be procured in advance, and the Veterinary Surgeon will advise as to what should be given for the first twenty-four hours or so according to what kind of operation has been performed. But it is safe to assume that honey and milk will be needed, and may be the only food which will be allowed to begin with. Since the dog very probably will be scarcely ' round ' from the anaesthetic he will need to be in a quiet room where he may sleep quietly and gradually come back to normal.

When fetching a dog who has undergone surgery, from the Veterinary Surgeon, it is advisable to take a carrying box if the dog is of a fairly small breed, and in the box there should be warm blankets and again hot water bottles. If the dog is one of a large breed, it is advisable to take a coat for him to wear and also ask a second person other than the driver of the car to accompany one, as although a dog may appear little. more than rather vague and drowsy, often he will suddenly indulge in spurts of wild energy, and this can be very dangerous if one is alone and driving the car. When not completely round from the anaesthetic he may also make a considerable noise, growling and howling, although he does not know he is doing this, and he needs then to be soothed and quietened. After an anaesthetic it may take anything up to twenty-four hours before the dog is steady on his legs, and therefore when going out to relieve himself he will need to be supported, as otherwise in his giddiness he may fall and injure himself. So make all these preparations in advance, as they will all help the dog to make a quicker recovery.

If the operation involved is a Caesarian, then a small box with warm bedding and a hot water bottle will also need to be taken with you for the puppies to be brought home in, and also a warm place prepared as the bitch may not be able to cope with her puppies for some hours. Though it is incredible how a bitch may well be feeding her babies within two hours of a Caesarian operation, before she is by any means round from the anaesthetic, and it is delightful to see her first rather drowsy and unsteady attempts at licking her new puppies. Sometimes a bitch may appear to turn against her new babies after a 'Caesar' and will growl and bare her teeth at any move they make. If this is so, she must not be left alone with them until she is completely round, and once more in her right mind. She does not really know what she is doing or what the puppies are, but this phase will pass, and it is better in this case to keep the puppies away from the dam for several hours, and this may involve feeding them on Lactol with a dropper until the bitch can take on her rightful job. So be prepared and have everything ready.

Certainly a dog after any form of surgery or anaesthetic, even if it is only a small matter of the extraction of a tooth or the lancing of an abscess, will suffer shock, and thus must be kept very warm and very quiet.

CHAPTER FOUR

VIRUS DISEASES IN DOGS

Symptoms – Immunisation – Booster Inoculations

THE THREAT of disease is always a worry to animal owners. In dogs, two particularly serious diseases are distemper and contagious hepatitis; both are caused by viruses.

The existence of viruses has been known since the end of the nineteenth century, but until comparatively recently it has not been possible to investigate the actual nature of the virus organism. The advent of the electro-microscope, together with the development of new techniques, has enabled research workers to forge ahead in the detailed study of viruses. There are many ideas as to what viruses really are. However, quite simply, they can be regarded as minute organisms, chemical rather than cellular in nature, which are capable of self-multiplication when they are in association with living cells.

The virus has to be within living tissue in order to develop; in doing so, the body cells involved are usually damaged or even killed. Viruses often show an affinity for particular tissues; thus they may attack specific organs of the body, causing the characteristic symptoms of the particular disease.

Canine distemper is world-wide in distribution. The age of the animal at the time of exposure to the disease is an important factor in determining the course of the disease. In very young puppies death may occur after only a few days, with the animals showing hardly any signs of illness. They may lose their appetite, appearing to have a chill, but then suddenly die.

As puppies get older, the ability to survive distemper infection appears to increase. There is usually the initial temperature rise, five to eight days after exposure to the disease. At this stage the animal usually appears alert and healthy. After a few days the temperature falls to normal; to be followed by a further rise severals days later. The animal now begins to show slight signs of distress, with symptoms such as mild diarrhoea and discharging from the eyes and nose. As a rule, the condition does not give the appearance of being serious until fairly late in the course of the infection. The symptoms may get progressively worse, with laboured breathing, coughing and possibly vomiting. Loss of appetite often follows and the dog can become dehydrated and emaciated. However, in a number of cases animals go through phases of apparent recovery, with the temperature falling to near normal. This alternating state may continue for a number of weeks, until in the majority of cases, a nervous condition, (associated with the infection of the brain by the virus) sets in. A hardening of the footpads sometimes occurs at this stage. Typical symptoms are convulsions, inco-ordination, depression, and paralysis. Later, a condition called chorea may appear, which is typified by twitching of one or more muscles. Animals do not, as a rule, recover fully from these nervous symptoms and have to be destroyed.

Contagious hepatitis is an infectious disease associated with damage to the liver. Although dogs of all ages are susceptible, the disease is more common in young animals. Symptoms do not arise until five to eight days after exposure to the disease. In a mild case, the only sign of hepatitis may be a rise in temperature lasting one or two days. However, in more acute cases a fiery redness of the mucous membranes of the mouth is seen in addition, together with intense thirst and sometimes abdominal pain. The disease is of very much shorter duration than distemper. The first twenty-four hours can be regarded as the most critical period; if the dog survives this it stands a good chance of recovery. In a matter of days the disease may have cleared up completely, although in a few dogs an opacity of the eye ('Blue Eye') develops after about ten days; this, as a rule, clears up after a short time.

If dogs injure themselves during illness they may bleed profusely from the site of the injury; this is because the damage that the virus causes to the liver upsets the blood clotting mechanism. Most dogs stand a good chance of recovery from the disease, although they usually take several weeks to regain weight and condition.

In spite of the most skilful treatment some dogs fail to make a satisfactory recovery from these diseases. Some animals die directly as a result of the diseases, but more have to be put to sleep in order to avoid extreme suffering. How then can dogs be protected? The answer: by vaccination. It will not be amiss for the dog owner to know something of the way in which the vaccine works and the method which nature has devised to protect young animals.

When an animal becomes infected by a disease, its body produces antibodies in the blood stream which serve to neutralise invading organisms, whether they be virsuses or bacteria. Once an animal has recovered from an infection, it is usually able to produce enough antibodies to ward off any further infection. By vaccination, we utilise this natural phenomenon by injecting the animal with organisms that have been suitably modified so as not to cause any diseases. However, the organism appears to the body as a dangerous invader and protective antibody is duly produced in an attempt to neutralise it. In this way we can make the animal immune to the disease without the risk of inducing an infection. Like everything in nature, the process is more involved than it seems and there are some animals that are just unable to produce antibodies, however many times they are vaccinated. For instance, in the same way that some humans do not respond to polio vaccination, some dogs fail to be immunised by distemper vaccination.

If a mother has been infected with the disease or vaccinated, she is able to confer protection upon her infants by passing on antibodies in her 'first-milk' or colostrum. These antibodies circulate in the young animals' blood until they gradually disappear. In this way the very young puppy can be immune from distemper and hepatitis in the first few months of its life. After this, vaccination is essential.

Vaccination has no effect if the puppy is inoculated while it has, in its blood, a high level of antibodies derived from its mother. Because of this, puppies are not vaccinated against distemper and hepatitis until they are about three months old. However, there are times when the Veterinary Surgeon may consider a different time safer, or may even recommend a second inoculation shortly after the first.

Once a puppy has been vaccinated against hepatitis, it is usually immune for life. However, with distemper, the immunity may in some cases only last a year or so. Under certain circumstances it may be advisable to have your dog revaccinated after a year. Your Veterinary Surgeon will be able to advise you on this point.

To sum up, remember that distemper and hepatitis are extremely serious diseases in dogs. If your dogs appears 'off colour' do not disregard it; keep a careful eye on the animal and take it to a Veterinary Surgeon if it does not improve after a day or so. Finally, it should be stressed that if your dog has not been vaccinated, make sure you see your Veterinary Surgeon about a suitable vaccination course right away.

CHAPTER FIVE

FIRST AID IN EMERGENCIES

Emergency Kit – Drowning – Eclampsia – Electric
Shock – Road Accidents

IN EMERGENCIES, there is little time to read up symptoms and treatments, therefore we would urge owners thoroughly to acquaint themselves with the immediate treatment necessary in any accident or trouble that might happen to a dog. Also it is a wise policy to have the necessary first aid remedy absolutely ready, possibly kept in a separate box marked in large letters ' EMERGENCY '. Again on the lid of such a box should be noted the Veterinary Surgeon's name, address and telephone number. In this box the following items should be kept:

Smelling Salts.
Bicarbonate of Soda.
Vinegar (small bottle).
Brandy (small bottle).
Glucose in small polythene bag.
Sedative Tablets (Sherley's).
Honey.
Collo-Cal-D.
Disprin Tablets.
Salt (small pieces in polythene bag).
Acriflavine Ointment.
Piece of string for Ligature or Tourniquet.
Pencil.
Permanganate of Potash Crystals.
Soda (small pieces in polythene bag).

Milk of Magnesia.
Roll of Bandage.
Cotton Wool.
Pair of Curved Scissors.
Pair of Nail Clippers.
Small pair of tweezers.
Small Box of ' Band-Aid '.

ASPHIXIA. This means that for some reason the air cannot get into the lungs and the dog cannot breathe – for instance in cases of drowning, coal gas poisoning, choking, etc. In drowning, water must be removed from lungs, in coal gas poisoning fresh air is essential and also smelling salts held under the nose, and in choking removal of the obstacle (see relevant paragraph), and in severe cases the Veterinary Surgeon must be called without delay. Artificial respiration should be given.

BURNS:
Acid Burns: Use bicarbonate of soda and water; one teaspoon in a cup of water. Swab liberally.
Alkali Burns: Use vinegar and water (50/50) or lemon juice. Acriflavine ointment is excellent for burns, or strong cold tea in an emergency. A bandage should be put on if possible as all air should be excluded from burns. Give the dog a sedative to ease pain. Keep quiet and feed on a light diet for several days.

CHOKING. Can be caused by a piece of biscuit or large piece of meat becoming lodged in the throat. Either try to pull out the obstacle, or else gently push down the throat. If bone in throat, call the Veterinary Surgeon.

COLLAPSE. Occurs after road accidents, or when poisoned or in Eclampsia (see relevant paragraph). The dog is practically unconscious, eyes are usually open and staring, the body and lips are cold, and the gums and tongue very pale. The breathing is heavy and slow. Keep the dog warm with rugs and hot water bottles wrapped in pieces of blanket or towel, and lie the dog on his *right* side. A few drops of neat brandy may be put on his tongue. No other liquids can be given by mouth until the dog is fully conscious again. Then glucose (one teaspoon in two tablespoonsful of water) may be given. Collapse is, of course, a symptom of some more serious illness or injury, and the Veterinary Surgeon should be called without delay.

CONVULSIONS. Often occur when puppies are teething, the puppy dropping to the floor, kicking and jerking, and with saliva coming from the mouth. Sometimes the puppy will urinate or pass a motion involuntarily. Cold water should be swabbed on to head and back of neck, and the puppy held until he recovers his senses. Then give a sedative, and keep very quiet in a darkened room for a few days, feeding a light milky diet. Also occurs in adults in cases of poisoning (see relevant paragraph) when it is serious and needs immediate Veterinary treatment.

DOG FIGHTS. Throw rug, coat, towel, etc. over the dogs, or else douse with a bucket of water. If only one person present, don't pick up one dog as the other dog involved will leap up and tear at the dog or yourself. If two people present, each dog should be picked up or held away with the rug or sack firmly over its head. Any bites received by dog or human should be washed with diluted T.C.P. or other good antiseptic.

DROWNING. A large dog should be laid on a table or a slope with the head hanging down. Small dogs should be held up by hind legs and shaken in an effort to remove water from the lungs. Artificial respiration should be employed, by placing hands gently but firmly on each side of the ribs, and pressing and depressing at the rate of about sixteen times a minute or in time with one's own breathing. Continue until dog is breathing normally again. In the case of a small dog, the ' Kiss of Life ' often succeeds. Breathe gently into the dog's mouth and then with-. draw the breath at the rate of normal breathing. The whole of the little dog's mouth and nostrils must be covered by one's own mouth. When the dog is recovering rub briskly with warm towels, and keep very warm and quiet.

ECLAMPSIA. Occurs with bitches who are feeding a litter, and usually when the puppies are about three weeks old, when the bitch is rather tired from the strain of feeding her babies. Occurs very occasionally in bitches just prior to whelping. It is caused by lack of calcium. The total amount of calcium in a bitch can be drawn off by puppies in twenty-four hours, and if she is debilitated she may not be able to produce enough calcium to replenish herself. The bitch starts to twitch in her shoulder muscles, and has a rather vague or wild look in her eyes, and then begins to pant. Swiftly the twitching increases all over her body until she falls down with all four legs jerking. The next stage is coma. This is a *very* urgent case for the Veterinary Surgeon, as if treatment is not forthcoming death can result. The Veterinary Surgeon will usually inject large quantities of Calcium Gluconate into the bitch, and recovery is mainly very rapid. Until the Veterinary Surgeon arrives, a dose of Collo-Cal-D should be given (from two teaspoons to two tablespoons according to the size of the bitch) and repeated in fifteen minutes. However, such liquid must not be given if the bitch has lapsed into unconsciousness. The bitch will have to be taken away from the puppies for some hours, and then should feed only one or two puppies in rotation for some days. Immediate supplementary feeding of Lactol by dropper, should be started with the puppies. Doses of Collo-Cal-D should be given to the bitch night and morning until the puppies are weaned.

ELECTRIC SHOCK. Do not touch the dog with your bare hands. Use rubber gloves and either put on rubber boots or stand on a rubber mat. Push wires or live electric surface away from the dog with a walking stick or piece of wood. Ensure such wood is absolutely dry, as water is a conductor of electricity. Keep the dog very warm and give a warm drink. Treat burns in the usual way.

FISH HOOKS. Do not attempt to pull these out. Cut the shank of the hook, and then draw the hook out backwards. Apply T.C.P. to the wound.

FITS AND HYSTERIA. Usually occur when puppies are teething or as an after effect of distemper. In highly strung dogs hysteria can be brought on by a loud and continuous sound such as a fire siren or hooter. Restrain the dog, and sponge head and back of neck with cold water. After he has more or less returned to normal, give a sedative and keep him in a darkened room, feeding on a light diet.

FRACTURES. These can occur fairly frequently, particularly in the small fine-boned breeds of dogs. Many causes are road accidents, jumping off tables or chairs, cannoning when playing. The dog screams, and the break is usually obvious from the awkward position in which the leg is held. The limb should be securely wrapped round with several layers of stiff corrugated paper and tied round with bandage or tape, and the dog taken immediately to the Veterinary Surgeon for examination, setting and plastering. There may be considerable shock and therefore the dog must be well wrapped up. After the plaster has been put on, the dog should be kept as quiet as possible, and fed on a light diet with plenty of honey and milk or honey and water to drink for a few days. Special watch must be kept to see that the foot does not swell below the plaster, and if this should happen, the Veterinary Surgeon must be informed at once. To test whether a limb is broken, the relevant elbow or thigh joint should be gently squeezed. If there is no reflex action and the foot remains flabby and limp, this usually means

FIG. 4.—Leg bandage (a) The foreleg for cases of strain or injury, (b) the hind leg, also for cases of strain or injury to the stifle. Adhesive plaster is used for the top half.

a fracture. If however the toe or foot contracts and stretches out, it means generally that no bone is broken, and just a severe sprain or strain has been suffered.

HEAT STROKE. Remove the dog immediately into a cool, shady spot, and apply a salt solution (one teaspoon of salt in one pint of cold water) to the head and back of the neck. Keep bathing these parts until the dog revives and is obviously recovering. A few drops of brandy on the tongue will help. Keep him in a cool and darkened room for twenty-four hours.

MISALLIANCE. When a bitch accidentally mates with an undesirable dog, there is no point in trying to force them apart as this may rupture both of them, and in any case the mating will probably have been effective in the first fifteen seconds. The bitch should be taken to the Veterinary Surgeon within forty-eight hours when an injection of Stilboestrol will nullify the conception of puppies. But the bitch will then recommence her season and will again be in a condition to mate between the ninth and fifteenth day of her heat, but usually she will not ' take ' in these circumstances. Such an injection very occasionally affects the bitch at the season six months later, and it may prove difficult to then get her in whelp. It is advantageous to give her a course of Vitamin E. Succinate, for a month before she is due in season again.

POISONING. This is a very wide subject, as so many things can poison a dog. Poisoning can cause shock, collapse and eventual death, and the swift attentions of the Veterinary Surgeon are most necessary. It is only possible here to give a broad outline of some of the properties which can poison a dog, and the first aid treatment.

Acids: Give Milk of Magnesia or salad oil.

Alkalis: Give milk, diluted vinegar, and eggs.

Arsenic: Give emetic, milk to drink and a purge. Brandy may be given as a stimulant. Rat poisons often contain arsenic.

Carbon Monoxide: Get the dog into fresh air immediately and fan him. Give brandy and apply artificial respiration.

Food: Give an emetic and strong aperient. Afterwards feed on arrowroot gruel and give honey and water to drink.

Lead: Often resulting from licking or chewing painted

objects. Give emetic immediately, and then feed on milk and honey.

Phosphorus: Again contained in some rat and mouse poisons. Give emetic and feed on honey and water. No milk or fatty and oily foods must be given.

Beware of all garden sprays, insecticides, pesticides, slug killers, etc. unless these definitely state that they are *not* dangerous for *children*. Many of such preparations state that they are safe with animals, but this is not always strictly correct, and many dogs can become seriously poisoned after picking up pellets, chicken or rat droppings etc.

Fig. 5.—An all-enveloping bag made of linen or calico to prevent the dog from chewing or worrying an injury to the legs or body.

ROAD ACCIDENTS. These occur all too often and call for immediate first aid and then Veterinary treatment. If a dog is hit by a car he suffers extreme fright, and even the most placid dog is liable to bite anyone who comes near, so be careful with a dog thus injured. If possible, take him firmly by the scruff of the neck and try to calm him by a soothing voice and gentle stroking with the hands. Don't move him if he is lying down unless this is absolutely necessary for traffic purposes. It is essential to get veterinary aid with the least possible delay. It is almost impossible to diagnose to what extent he is injured when he is in a state of fright and shock. He may have severe internal injuries, or he may have come off lightly with only a few bruises. Until the Veterinary Surgeon arrives, the dog should be covered with warm coats, rugs or blankets, and should be soothed as much as possible. No liquids of any sort should be given. If fractures are apparent in one or more of the legs, try to keep the limb as immobile as possible. If a bad gash has been sustained, hold a pad on this to stop bleeding as much as possible. If the bleeding is very profuse this may mean that an artery or a vein has been injured or severed. If the blood is bright red and spurting in fast jets this indicates an artery, and a tourniquet must be applied just above the wound, and nearest the heart. But if the blood is dark red and oozing profusely this points to an injured vein, and then the tourniquet must be applied below the wound and furthest from the heart. A tourniquet *must* be loosened every ten minutes, otherwise great damage will be caused. (See relevant paragraph on fixing a tourniquet).

If there is no possibility of getting a Veterinary Surgeon then the dog must be taken to the nearest surgery or Animal Clinic, or the R.S.P.C.A. contacted. The dog must then be lifted most gently on to a flat board or tray, and put into a car, and kept covered and warm with blankets.

SCALDS. Anoint the burn with Acriflavine ointment immediately, and keep the place covered if possible. Give the dog a Disprin if suffering much pain. If the skin is blistered this must be kept very clean, as it can become septic. If the scald is very severe, burns may be considerable and collapse may even occur. Veterinary treatment would then be necessary.

SHOCK. This may be experienced in any condition which causes a great deal of pain or fright, or loss of blood. The signs of shock are a feeble pulse, slow heart beat and very shallow breathing. The dog should be kept as warm as possible with blankets and hot water bottles,

A few drops of brandy in a little water may be given, and smelling salts will help the condition.

SNAKE OR ADDER BITES. These cause great pain and a certain amount of fright to the dog. The actual place of the bite can be seen, and a tight ligature should be applied (if the bite is on a limb) just above the wound. The wound should then be cut into with a sharp knife, and Permanganate of Potash crystals pressed firmly into the wound. The dog must be kept moving in an effort to prevent him from becoming sleepy or comatose. Stimulants such as brandy and water, strong black coffee or strong tea should be spooned down his throat until Veterinary help arrives.

In all cases of sudden accident or injury, try to get someone else to telephone the Veterinary Surgeon, and stay yourself by the side of your dog. You will be able to give him a great deal of reassurance and comfort by just talking to him and gently stroking him. Try not to show that you are anxious, as this is very easily transferred to the dog. It is essential that he should remain as quiet as possible until the Veterinary Surgeon arrives, and he is more likely to do this if he knows you are by his side.

WASP STINGS. Can be very dangerous as the dog is inclined to snap at wasps, or else tread on them, and suffer a bad sting. A large-necked jar should be kept available during the spring and summer, containing a solution made up of two tablespoonsful of bicarbonate of soda dissolved in a pint of water. If stung on the foot, this should be put right into the bottle for several minutes. If the sting is on the body, the affected part should be continuously swabbed with the solution. Alternatively rub the place with a piece of ordinary washing soda.

CHAPTER SIX

FIRST AID IN
EVERY DAY AILMENTS

Symptoms and First Treatments

ABSCESSES AND BOILS. *Symptoms:* A small lump appears, containing pus. This is most painful to the touch. *Treatment:* This may be brought to a head with the application of poultices such as Kaolin or Antiphlogistine, and at the right moment opened by the Veterinary Surgeon. Quite a large, deep hole may be left after the poison has been removed, which must be kept soft until healed. It will aid healing if the hole is packed with gauze soaked in diluted T.C.P. A tonic is advisable after the dog has suffered from an abcess or a boil and Sherleyvites or Cytacon are recommended.

BRONCHITIS. *Symptoms:* Difficulty in breathing, cough, and some wheezing. *Treatment:* Keep the dog in a warm dry place. A steaming kettle with a piece of lint soaked in Eucalyptus oil in the spout, will help. Daily doses of Owbridges Cough Mixture are excellent. Diet should be light and bowels kept open. An aperient such as Rhubarb Tablets (Herb Royal Ltd.), or Lik-a-Med (Sherley's) is good. If temperature rises to any extent, say over 102.5°, the Veterinary Surgeon should be called.

BRUISES. *Symptoms:* Discolouration of the skin caused by an injury. *Treatment:* Frequent bathing with Tincture of Arnica diluted in warm water (dessertspoonful to half a pint of water). If the dog is very restless and obviously suffering pain, a Disprin may be given.

CHILLS. *Symptoms:* Slightly upset tummy, a little shivering, lack of energy, sometimes sneezing and a slight discharge from the nose. *Treatment:* Keep warm, feed on a light diet, and give a Disprin every four hours. But owners must be warned that these symptoms could equally mean the commencement of some more serious illness such as distemper, therefore the dog should be isolated and watched very carefully, and temperature checked daily. It is unlikely that much rise of temperature would occur from a common chill.

COLIC. *Symptoms:* The dog is restless, whines in pain, and continually flicks round to look at his tummy or side. It is usually caused by indigestion or flatulence. *Treatment:* Relief is caused if the dog can pass a motion, and it is sometimes helpful to insert a glycerine suppository into the rectum, for this purpose. Equally the pain might be caused by some foreign body in the abdomen, and possibly only an X-ray can discover this. If the condition does not clear up fairly quickly, the Veterinary Surgeon should be asked for his opinion.

CONSTIPATION. *Symptoms:* The dog strains and only achieves a result after some time, and then the motions will be dry and crumbly and difficult to pass. *Treatment:* If a little All-Bran can be included in the diet this will usually put the dog right. Otherwise aperients such as Rhubarb Tablets (Herb Royal) or Lik-a-Med (Sherley's). But it is better to aim at remedying the cause rather than curing the symptoms, and thus diet should be well considered. Raw meat will help, also liver, and brown bread instead of biscuits, with added green vegetable. Aperients with a strong purging action such as castor oil or liquid paraffin, should never be given.

COUGHS. *Symptoms:* A hard dry cough points to a

heart condition, while a loose cough with accompanying retching indicates a chill. *Treatment:* For the first type, the Veterinary Surgeon should be consulted; but in the second type regular doses of Owbridges Lung Tonic are excellent. Honey and milk should be given twice a day (a dessertspoon of honey in a cup of warm milk). The dog should be watched for any rise in temperature as a cough can also be the first symptoms in distemper. Keep warm and out of draughts until recovered.

DANDRUFF. *Symptoms:* The dog's coat is full of grey particles of scurf. This may be caused by the fact that the soap was not properly rinsed from the coat during a recent bath, or may be due to worms, or the presence of fleas or lice. *Treatment:* In the first case, the dog should be re-bathed, special attention being given to rinsing. To help in rinsing, a small quantity of lemon juice or vinegar may be added to the water. In the second and third cases see under ' Pests and Parasites ' chapter. In any case, the coat would much benefit by a course of Sherley's Coatacine, to get it into condition again.

DIARRHOEA. On no account should one attempt to stop diarrhoea, as it is nearly always the outward sign of some inward poisoning which needs evacuating. It could be the first signs of distemper, worms, a chill etc., and thus other symptoms should be looked for in the hope of diagnosing the real cause. If the diarrhoea is caused by something in the diet, it will quickly pass. The very fact that the dog has diarrhoea is in itself a good thing, as it means that he is in process of getting rid of the poison or whatever is upsetting him. But breeders should beware of any ' stopping up ' medicine such as chalk, which only contrives to ' cork ' the dog, and the poison then runs riot in the body. Any case of diarrhoea accompanied by a rise in temperature, should be checked by the Veterinary

Surgeon, in case it is the forerunner of some serious complaint.

DISCHARGES. There are several discharges which may need attention.

Vaginal discharge. Symptoms: After having produced a litter, a bitch may suffer a messy, dark bloody discharge from the vagina. Also a bitch may produce a persistent creamy discharge after finishing her season. Either type of discharge is very weakening and should receive attention. *Treatment:* In both cases, syringing the vagina with a solution of Amplexol (Ashe Laboratories Ltd.) will help, but both are conditions which need veterinary treatment. If a bitch has been mated, and commences a discharge of blood about two weeks later, this usually indicates that she is in process of aborting the expected puppies. Immediate and large injections of penicillin may save the litter, and thus the Veterinary Surgeon should be consulted immediately.

Rectal discharge. Could be a foreign body in the rectum, or a discharge from anal glands, or an intestinal infection. Cleaning of anal glands should be carried out, and if no improvement the Veterinary Surgeon's advice should be sought.

Mouth discharge. Usually indicates a bad tooth, and examination should be made.

Ear discharge. Usually a symptom of canker. See ' Care of Ears ', chapter.

Penis discharge. The penis discharge is a mattery liquid. This condition is known as Balanitis. The part should be well syringed out twice a day with a solution of Amplexol or T.C.P., (as recommended for a gargle).

Nose discharge. If thick, yellow mucous, this may point to distemper. The dog must be examined, as a serious virus disease may be present. Sometimes in Hard

Pad disease, the dog's nose discharges a clear water-like fluid, but the other signs of this disease are also present, and it cannot be confused with the cold, wet nose of the healthy dog.

Discharge from Cuts, Wounds, etc. This is serum discharging from the broken skin. Should be bathed with saline solution (one teaspoon of salt to a cup of warm water) or diluted T.C.P., but the best healing agents are fresh air and the dog's own saliva.

GASTRITIS. *Symptoms:* The dog will continually vomit, the content being a frothy white mucous. The dog has an abnormal thirst. *Treatment:* Food should be withheld and the dog should be given honey and cold boiled water only. (A dessertspoon of honey to a small cup of water.) The vomiting is very weakening and no time must be lost in stopping this. Bismuth is useful, but it is a malady which needs immediate veterinary attention, as it could be the forerunner of the more serious Gastroenteritis and Leptospirosis.

HAEMORRHAGE. (Internal.) May occur when the dog has been injured in an accident. *Symptoms:* The gums become very pale, the pulse very slow and weak, and the dog sighs continually as he breathes. Contact the Veterinary Surgeon immediately and meanwhile keep the dog quiet and immobile, and as warm as possible. Bleeding from nose, rectum and limbs also may occur after severe accident, and there should be great haste to get a Veterinary Surgeon. (See Chapter II regarding tourniquets.)

HERNIA. There are three types of hernia—umbilical, inguinal and scrotal. *Symptoms:* Umbilical hernia is a small protrusion of the bowel at the navel, and is not very often serious providing it is small and pliable. Often found in puppies. A penny wrapped in cotton wool and placed over the hernia and strapped to the abdomen with plaster, may effect a complete cure within a few days. Inguinal hernia, only met with in bitches, is a swelling in the groin, and as it tends to get bigger, should receive surgical treatment.

Scrotal hernia is a swelling in the scrotum, usually on the right side. It varies in size, but is larger in a stout dog, and is larger after a heavy meal. Operation for this condition can be carried out.

HICCUP. Quite often experienced in puppies. Often caused by bolting food too quickly, or becoming excessively hungry. Occasionally the adult dog suffers from hiccups. This is not usually a serious complaint, and milk of magnesia will generally obviate any further symptoms.

INDIGESTION. *Symptoms:* The dog is restless, and unable to remain in one position. The tummy rumbles and squeaks. *Treatment:* As the cause is usually that the dog has either eaten too rich food, or has eaten too much, the best remedy is to withhold all food and drink for several hours. A dose of milk of magnesia is most useful, and as a first meal, milk and honey is very soothing to the stomach. The squeaking noises in the tummy might equally be caused by worms, but is not so likely with an adult dog. Frequently a dog with indigestion will eat quite a lot of grass, which makes him vomit. This is nature's way, and he will usually then recover quickly.

JAUNDICE. *Symptoms:* The dog is completely off his food, there is great lethargy, severe thirst and also continuous vomiting. Later on, a distinct yellow tinge is noted in the whites of the eyes and in the gums. It is usually the forerunner of Leptospirosis. *Treatment:* Immediate contact with Veterinary Surgeon for diagnosis and treatment, as the dog can go into a coma and swiftly die. Large injections of penicillin or leptospira serum may help to fight the disease.

NETTLERASH (*Urticaria*): *Symptoms:* The dog's face, eyelids, lips, ears and genitals, all swell and are hot to the touch. It is thought to be caused by allergy to certain foods, and sometimes from various insect bites, or even from being severely stung by nettles. Usually the condition passes fairly quickly. *Treatment:* The injection of adrenalin solution by the Veterinary Surgeon expedites recovery. Occasionally the dog may suffer collapse after treatment, and then a strong solution of glucose (one teaspoon glucose in two tablespoonsful of water) will bring the dog swiftly to himself again.

NEURALGIA. *Symptoms:* The dog is obviously in sudden and great pain, and the muscles of the neck, or back, or legs are very tense, according to where the neuralgia is being experienced. The attacks are usually intermittent, lasting possibly some hours at a time. *Treatment:* The dog must be kept warm and as quiet as possible. Disprin should be given every three hours. An infra-red ray lamp gives great comfort to the dog. If the pain becomes excessive the Veterinary Surgeon should be consulted, when possibly injections or tablets of Leucotropine may be prescribed.

NIPPLES SORENESS. A condition which often occurs when a bitch is half-way through feeding a litter. Usually caused by the puppies' nails pricking the soft flesh of the teats. *Treatment:* The nails on the front feet of the puppies should be cut short once a week. A little vaseline should be applied to the nipples of the bitch twice a day. This should be very well rubbed in, and any surplus wiped off with cotton wool or a tissue. Where the nipples have become cracked, these should be bathed with a lotion made up of half a teaspoonful of boracic acid and half a pint of water. Dry well afterwards and use vaseline.

PLEURISY. *Symptoms:* Very difficult and quick breathing, and a rise in temperature. Any pressure on the ribs obviously causes the dog pain. *Treatment:* It is an illness that requires the attention of the Veterinary Surgeon, and there is little one can do as home treatment, except keep the dog warm and quiet, and feed on a light diet.

PNEUMONIA. Not very common in dogs, and less so nowadays when antibiotics help so much. *Symptoms:* Intense shivering with a high temperature. The breathing is difficult, and the dog gives a peculiar grunt when breathing. Occasionally there is a cough, and the chest area is painful to the touch. *Treatment:* The Veterinary Surgeon should be contacted quickly, as early administration of penicillin or one of its variants will effect a speedy cure. The dog must be kept warm and quiet, and fed on a light diet. Honey and milk is an excellent mixture at such times, and should be given thrice daily. A pneumonia coat should be worn.

PROLAPSE OF THE BOWEL. A condition which occurs with puppies. It can be an effect of worm infestation. *Symptoms:* The puppy strains to pass a motion, and a small portion of intestine protrudes from the rectum. *Treatment:* This should be gently bathed with warm water, and then the protruding piece gently pressed back with a wad of cotton wool. The entrance to the rectum should be carefully lubricated with vaseline or olive oil. If the protruding piece does not easily return into the rectum, then the Veterinary Surgeon should be called immediately, as it is a dangerous condition and can cause the dog or puppy a lot of pain.

SPRAINS. These can happen in a second, but are difficult to locate. The most usual place for a sprain or strain in a puppy or adult dog is either the shoulder or the stifle (knee joint). *Symptoms:* The dog usually cannot bear any weight on the injured limb, and limps or hops about. *Treatment:* Hot and cold formentations alternatively, relieve the condition, but really complete rest is the only answer. Thus a light diet is needed, and since the dog can take little exercise, his bowels should be watched, and probably a mild aperient such as Rhubarb Tablets, or Lik-a-Med, should be given if necessary.

TRAVEL SICKNESS. Not a great many dogs suffer from this condition, but when they do it can be quite severe and most inconvenient if taking a dog by car or train. *Symptoms:* The dog commences by yawning frequently, and then produces much saliva and dribbles constantly, and after that he continually vomits. He may also suffer from sudden and severe diarrhoea. *Treatment:* Sherley's Travel Sickness Tablets are excellent, and for best results the tablets should be given an hour before starting on a journey. Some owners have found that a good drink of cold milk half an hour before a journey completely obviates travel sickness, providing an antacid for this acid condition. It is certainly worth trying.

VAGINA (*stricture of*). Occasionally it is impossible for a dog to serve a bitch, for the reason that the bitch has a stricture of the vagina. Experienced breeders are able to dilate the bitch by the use of fingers, but unless the owner of the bitch is knowledgeable in this respect, it would be advisable to call the Veterinary Surgeon to perform the necessary dilation.

WARTS. These can occur on nearly any part of the dog's body. They provide a certain amount of irritation to the dog at times. They can usually be removed quite satisfactorily by surgery, and small warts which have a definite 'neck' can be removed by tying a steri- lised piece of cotton or silk as a ligature round the neck of the wart. Warts on eyelids should be removed by surgery, otherwise the dog may injure his eyes by rubbing or pawing. Warts should not be cauterised.

WOUNDS. There are many kinds of wounds. A punctured wound is probably the most dangerous and can be suffered by the dog in a fight, or from a rat or cat bite. A lacerated wound is when the skin is broken and torn, and may be caused by the dog being caught by wire netting, barbed wire, etc. A contused wound is when there is extensive bruising as well as an open wound, and is usually caused by bad falls or from being hit by a car.

In all cases, the hair should be carefully cut away from around the wound, and the part swabbed out with either a solution of Dettol or else T.C.P. Any pieces of grit, glass or other irritant should be carefully removed with steri- lised forceps. If there is very extensive bleeding, and if the wound is on one of the limbs, then it may be necessary to apply a tourniquet, (see Chapter II). This must be loosened every ten minutes for certain. No ointments of any kind should be used on wounds. Bathing with a mild disinfectant and then leaving uncovered, is by far the best treatment. In all cases of wounds, other than a simple cut, veterinary treatment should be sought.

CHAPTER SEVEN

ROUTINE MAINTENANCE

Care of Ears, Eyes, Teeth, Nails and Anal Glands

E AR S . T H E S E should be inspected once a week, and dusted with a little Sherley's Canker Powder (puffer tin) as a precaution against any infection. If any sign of Canker appears, the ears should be very gently cleaned out with cotton wool wound on a match stick which has been dipped in olive oil. This softens any hard lumps, and the ears should then be easy to clean. Wipe off any oil that remains with cotton wool, and then dust with the canker powder. If the ears are badly infected, and make a 'squelching' noise when touched, then this will need rather more treatment, and in some cases will take quite a time to cure. Sherley's Canker Lotion capsules are very good, and will cure the complaint in time. However, if the canker is extremely obstinate, and the dog's ear is obviously very painful, then the Authors would also recommend the Ryotin Treatment, prepared by the Rybar Laboratories, Tankerton, Kent.

The treatment consists of first cleaning out the ear and then putting a few drops from the bottle of liquid into the ear night and morning for seven days. For the second part of the treatment, the ear must be dusted well with the powder supplied, for a further week. It is essential that the treatment is carried out absolutely according to instructions, and it is then successful in nearly every case. If the dog is obviously suffering a lot of pain in the ears, and is continually scratching the ear and walking about restlessly, a Disprin tablet should be given half an hour before each treatment is commenced. A great deal of ear trouble is caused by the presence of tiny mites in the channel, and as these can be passed from dog to dog, it is essential that others who come in contact with the infected dog should have the ears dusted with canker powder every day as a precaution. It is also important to plug dogs' ears with cotton wool before bathing, as water seeping down the ear channel can also set up a painful discharge. The best type of cotton wool to use is the *non-absorbent* kind, and if a little vaseline is smeared on the wool before insertion, this will prevent any water seeping down.

FIG. 6.—A cap made of linen or calico to prevent the dog from scratching the ears or injuring the ear flaps.

EYES. Dogs' eyes in the normal way need little attention beyond a weekly washing over with diluted Witch Hazel lotion, or else a solution of one teaspoonful of ordinary salt in a cup of warm water. However, dogs do occasionally suffer from conjunctivitis, when the white of the eye appears bloodshot and congested, and then after washing off with Witch Hazel, a thin streak of Golden Eye Ointment should be squeezed on to the eye-ball, the eye closed and gently massaged for a few seconds. This should be done daily. Sometimes a dog may suffer from a burn on the eye, either from sitting too near to a fire, or else from a tiny spark hitting the eye. This may cause a small ulcer about the size of a pin's head to appear on the eye-ball, or alternatively the eye may become com-

pletely clouded over. In any burns of this type, the eye
should be bathed with cold tea once or twice a day and
a little Golden Eye Ointment smeared on the lids. The
ulcer will eventually fade away, although in most cases
a minute dent in the eye-ball will remain. If the eye has
clouded this will clear again after several days. Occasionally a dog will get a cold in the eye from being out in a
strong wind, or from standing in a very draughty place,
and again the eye may cloud over, but Witch Hazel
lotion and Golden Eye Ointment will usually clear the
trouble swiftly. For any more serious eye injury, such as
when the dog runs into something like wire, or a stick,
or has an eye injured in a fight, then a Veterinary Surgeon should be called immediately, and until expert help
arrives the dog should be held still with a pad of Witch
Hazel lotion and cold water kept on the eye. In any severe
feverish disease or illness, the eyes tend to become congested and small beads of pus appear in the corner of the
eye, and the lids may become sticky and unable to be
opened, and in these cases the eyes should be gently
swabbed out as above once or twice a day and a smear of
Golden Eye ointment squeezed on to the eye. Some dogs
suffer from weeping eyes, and this condition is especially
noticeable in white dogs as the weeping causes a most
unsightly reddish stain where the tears have run down
the cheeks. This can be caused by a blocked tear duct, in
which case the Veterinary Surgeon will be needed. It
has also been noticed that the condition occurs in late
Spring and early Summer, and thus may be due to allergy
to pollen or dust, rather equivalent to Hay Fever in the
human. It also appears when the dog is run down or a
little out of sorts, or in a bitch when she is coming into
season or has just completed the feeding of a family. If
it is an allergy, then it is difficult to treat and the Veterinary Surgeon should be consulted. But it may greatly help
to give a fortnight's treatment with 'Diamond Eye',

which is an excellent lotion for this condition, prepared by 'Vitacoat Ltd.', 34, Selsdon Road, South Croydon. Another theory is that this unsightly condition may be due to acidity, and then 'Milk of Magnesia' daily will help, together with applications of 'Diamond Eye'.

TEETH. Most dogs have good teeth, and especially if they are brought up from early puppyhood to gnaw bones and hard biscuits. The feeding of knobs of raw meat will also help to keep the teeth clean and white.

FIG. 7.—A cool and light bandage improvised from a hairdressing net to keep dressings to the head or eye in place.

However, at times treatment for the teeth is necessary. Puppies do not suffer much discomfort when cutting their first teeth at about three weeks of age, but sometimes the second teeth which are cut at about four to five months of age do give the young dog a lot of pain, and it will be seen that the gums are a bright fiery red and the youngster is very off his food. Rubbing the gums with well diluted T.C.P. affords much relief, and the puppy should be given as much hard tack to gnaw as possible, such as bones, hard rubber rings, hard biscuits, etc. Occasionally the second teeth begin to appear before the first teeth have fallen out, and thus a second row of teeth is visible. This does not cause much trouble, except in the case of the long eye teeth, and if the baby canines do not fall out after some time, they should be removed by the Veterinary Surgeon. Occasionally a puppy may suffer from Teething Fits, and should this happen a light sedative such as Disprin should be given for a day or so, and the puppy kept as quiet as possible until the teeth are through. A dog who has toothache will usually paw his mouth and rub his face along the ground, and he may also stand still with his eyes slightly closed, occasionally champing his jaws or shaking his head. The mouth should then be examined, and if any teeth are loose or if the gums are very fiery, then the Veterinary Surgeon should be called to see if an extraction is necessary. Some dogs suffer from brown tartar on the teeth, which is usually caused by incorrect feeding, but if a dog's teeth are regularly cleaned this should not occur. An excellent tooth cleanser is a mixture of half Peroxide of Hydrogen (10 vols) and half cold milk, cotton wool dipped in and well swabbed round the teeth once a week. Alternatively, Eucryl tooth paste and a soft baby tooth brush can be used. If the tartar has been allowed to get really bad, then the teeth will need scaling and this should be carried out by the Veterinary Surgeon while the dog is under a mild anaesthetic. Occasionally a dog may have a painful abscess under a tooth, and this usually occurs in connection with the top molars, and an abscess about the size of a pea can be felt below the eye. Such an abscess is usually opened by the Veterinary Surgeon and drained, but it is a very painful condition for the dog. If a dog is suffering from a severe virus disease or feverish condition, the teeth may become furred with slimy brown substance, and this should not be confused with tartar which is hard and brittle. If a dog is very seriously ill, one cannot upset him by much teeth cleaning, and in this case swabbing gently with diluted fresh lemon juice and water will give him relief. Dogs suffer also from Pyorrhoea, when the gums are infected and recede from the teeth, leaving the teeth loose and painful. This should not happen with the dog whose teeth have been regularly cleaned. It usually means that the teeth will have to be extracted, and the gums freed of infection, but Peroxide and milk is a very good means of keeping the gums clean and healthy, and should obviate Pyorrhoea from developing.

NAILS. These need to be cut every week or so, though many dogs if they have correct hard exercise will naturally wear down their nails and will not need to have them cut. When cutting nails great care should be taken not to

Fig. 8.—A bandage for use in cases of severe canker or after an ear operation when the ear flap must not be bound closely to the inner part of the ear.

cut too near the quick. In a white dog the quick is easily recognised as the pale pink line which comes down to between an eighth of an inch and three quarters of an inch of the end of the nail (according to whether the nails need cutting or not) and it is essential not to cut this quick as it will bleed profusely. If this should happen, the dog's nail should be dipped into Permanganate of Potash crystals which will immediately stop the bleeding. Top show dogs often have their nails filed in order to produce compact, well muscled toes. For this purpose the nails should be filed every day, and the quick then recedes and very short nails can be attained. Dogs occasionally suffer with their dewclaws, when these have not been removed when young. They should be inspected every so often as if neglected they can curl round like a ram's horn and grow back into the flesh. They should be clipped in the normal way just below the quick.

FEET. Feet should be inspected regularly to make sure that no small sharp stones have become wedged between the pads. Such stones should be picked out and the pads washed in diluted T.C.P. Sometimes the pads become cracked and sore, and the very best treatment is to dust the pads every day with Sherley's Canker powder. Do not soak the feet in this case. Another rather painful condition is the presence of small cysts between the toes. These are extremely painful to the dog, and are generally thought to be caused by small mites or parasites working up between the toes. The small cysts become very red and inflamed, and after poulticing should be opened by the Veterinary Surgeon. These cysts attack dogs when they are in a rather low state of health, when the blood is in poor condition. A course of ' Sherleyvites ' should be given after the boils have burst or been opened, and while they are actually coming up a cooling medicine is essential, such as Flowers of Sulphur on the food, or else Sherley's Cooling Tablets.

ANAL GLANDS. These are two small glands situated just on the side of the rectal opening and they need regular attention. They secrete a certain amount of very obnoxious fluid which must be squeezed out every few months. If this necessary maintenance is neglected, a dog often as a result suffers from extremely painful abscesses. The symptoms of anal glands needing attention are that the dog will drag his behind along the ground, and will constantly jump as though he had been pricked, and will lick the anus. It is quite a simple thing to clean out the glands, but the Authors would advise owners to watch this being done by a Veterinary Surgeon or other competent person the first time, as it requires a definite knack and if clumsily carried out can make the dog very sore, and indeed could injure him severely. After the glands have been squeezed into a pad of cotton wool, the anus should be swabbed over with T.C.P. diluted with five parts water, the place dried and a smear of vaseline applied.

It must really be stressed that regular and efficient maintenance of ears, eyes, teeth and nails is of paramount importance, and if inspection and preventative measures against trouble are faithfully carried out, your dog will be saved constant irritation and possibly quite a lot of pain in his old age.

CHAPTER EIGHT

PESTS AND SKIN DISEASES

Fleas – Lice – Ticks – Worms – Mange

VARIOUS PARASITES do attack dogs from time to time, but most of these are easily got rid of and it is mostly a matter of recognition and then swift and efficient action. Dogs do not normally scratch unless they are actually changing their coats. When the new coat is coming through, the old and dead hair is pushed out and this does tend to overheat the skin and thus cause a certain amount of irritation. But if a dog is persistently scratching his coat, with the exception of the above reason, it may mean that he is harbouring parasites of some sort or another. But normally the dog who is bathed in a good insecticidal shampoo at reasonable intervals should put up a good resistance to pests. We would strongly recommend that dogs should be bathed at intervals of approximately four to six weeks in 'Vitacoat Antiscurf Shampoo', obtainable from Vitacoat Ltd., (Mr. Charles Warren) of 34, Selsdon Road, South Croydon. In between baths, dogs may be dusted with either Sherley's 'No-Scratch' which is supplied in a puffer tin, or else 'Vamoose' dusting powder, also in a puffer tin and obtainable from the Sherley's Division, Ashe Laboratories, Leatherhead, Surrey. For large smooth coated dogs where it is not too easy to carry out moderately frequent bathing these can be wiped down with a sponge soaked in 'Amplexol', and rubbed with a rough towel. 'Amplexol' is also obtainable from Ashe Laboratories. Another hygienic precaution, and a very necessary one, is that all blankets and rugs must be changed frequently. All beds, baskets, boxes should be washed over once a month and either sprayed with disinfectant or dusted with disinfectant powder. The onslaught of pests appears to a greater extent when the weather turns warmer in late Spring.

FLEAS. These horrid little pests cause a lot of irritation in dogs, and are also a frequent cause of worms, since they act as hosts to both round and tape worms. Dust

FIG. 9.—Pests (1) The common dog flea. The male is very small, and the female considerably larger. (2) The dog louse, greyish in colour. Both insects can be seen with the naked eye.

with 'Vamoose' or 'No Scratch' powder at intervals of seven days. The small fleas are males and the larger, lighter brown insects are females. If the dog still continues to scratch after applying the powder, then some other cause must be considered.

LICE. These parasites are more serious than fleas and cause greater irritation and are also a little more difficult to remove. They burrow into the skin and continuously suck small quantities of blood, but 'Vamoose' powder has great penetrating power through the somewhat tough shells of lice and usually clears the dog if perseverance is used. They usually hibernate in Winter and make their appearance again in the Spring. They congregate especially round the ears and round the root of the tail and under the tummy.

HARVEST MITES. A source of almost maddening irritation to the dog. These tiny mites look rather like grains of cayenne pepper and are seen round the nose, behind the elbows, round the ankles and on the belly. They also burrow into the hair round the pads of the foot, causing the dog to be continually gnawing and biting his foot. They are particularly to be found in latish Summer around harvest time. 'Vamoose' again is a sure cure and deterrent. If the insect powder has not been able to cure the dog of scratching, then we must look for something more serious, and must consider one or other of the specific skin diseases.

TICKS. Another of the pests that occasionally attack the dog in the Summer. They are normally to be found on sheep and cattle, but they lay their eggs in long grass, and it is thus very easy for the dog to pick up these pests when exercising where cattle have grazed. The ticks immediately fasten on to the skin of the dog and commence to suck his blood, and in a day or two the body of the tick will be about the size of a garden pea, and will be bluish in colour. This tick, which is really a swollen bladder of blood, fastens its head into the dog's flesh and is difficult to remove. The tick must not be pulled off as it will then leave its head still fixed in the dog, and this after a short while will cause a small lump of pus to form rather like a boil. There are various ways of making the tick loosen its grip on the dog, and one of the best is to hold a lighted cigarette to the swollen body of the tick and it will immediately loosen its hold and can be quickly knocked off. Another way of removal is to apply chloroform or methylated spirits to the tick and this again causes it to loose its hold. When the parasite has been drawn out it should be burnt, and the place on the skin of the dog where the head had burrowed should be dabbed with neat T.C.P. or Dettol. It is usual to find only one or two ticks on a dog, but just occasionally he may become completely infested, in which case he must be washed in Sherley's Insecticidal Shampoo and not rinsed but left with the shampoo still in his coat for ten minutes. The unrinsed coat should then be dried either with a rough towel, in the sun, or in front of a fire or with a hair dryer. The following day the dog's coat should be sprayed with Sherley's ' Supersect' which will kill any remaining eggs, and will act as a repellant to any further ticks with which the dog may come in contact.

WORMS. Worms are a nuisance and many dogs always seem to harbour them right from the moment they are born, and indeed even when they are still in their mother's womb. And although worms can cause divers diseases and illnesses, some dogs and puppies appear to be completely oblivious of the presence of these parasites.

(a) *Worms in puppies:* Usually these are thread worms or round worms. The symptoms are often either a ravenous or a choosey appetite, a dull eye, a staring coat, motions which are loose and usually containing a certain amount of jelly, and sometimes a ' pot belly '. Any puppy showing any of these signs should be suspect. He should first have his temperature taken and if this is between 101.5° and 102.5° then it is safe to worm him. All puppies should be wormed at six to eight weeks of age and again between twelve and fourteen weeks of age. After that it may be necessary to worm once a year, but the owner must be guided by the condition of the dog and the advice of the Veterinary Surgeon. It is wise, in any case, to obtain the necessary worm dose from the Veterinary Surgeon as he will prescribe according to the *age* and *weight* of the puppy or adult dog to be dosed. In these days, worm doses do not purge the dog as they used to do, causing him to turn out quantities of wriggling worms. Modern day worm doses such as 'Anti-ban', 'Banocide,' or 'Cooperane' etc. kill the worm eggs and the actual worms disintegrate and are passed through, and thus one seldom sees any evidence of the actual presence of worms. Such tablets, which are usually marked as one tablet for every eight or ten pounds body weight of

FIG. 10.—Worms. (1) Tape worm showing (*a*) the head of the worm, and (*b*) the tail of the worm breaking off in segments. (2) Round or Puppy worms, which may be tightly coiled if still alive, or straight if dead, and pointed at each end.

the dog, should be given half an hour after the dog has had a small breakfast. Occasionally the dog may vomit after being given the dose, but usually the dose has gone down far enough and this will not affect its efficiency. If it is not possible to obtain specific tablets from the Veterinary Surgeon, Sherley's Round Worm Capsules are extremely good. Round worms are easily recognised as they are pink, cream or greyish in colour, pointed at both ends and usually measure between three and six inches. Thread worms look like coils of white cotton thread.

(b) *Worming Mated Bitches:* As a preventative of worms in puppies, it helps to dose the bitch ten days after mating – or in fact, immediately her season ends. It is not advisable to worm a mated bitch later than three weeks after mating, as this could cause her to abort her litter.

The appropriate dose should be obtained from the Veterinary Surgeon.

(c) *Tape Worms:* These are much more serious and usually only affect the grown dog. They are quite easily detected for whitish-grey segments (looking very like grains of rice) adhere to the hair on the dog's anus, and can also be seen in the motions. If a dog is really badly infested, then strings of flat greyish 'tape' will be seen hanging from the rectum and yards of this can be pulled away. Dogs cannot actually 'catch' or pick up worms from each other, as the worm must have an intermediary host — and this host is usually the flea (hence the importance of keeping dogs free from fleas) who eats the tape worm eggs, the fleas then incubate the head of a tape worm, the dog eats the flea and the tape worm grows and flourishes in the dog. It is essential to rid your dog of tape worm if you are sure he harbours this pest because tape worms can lead to many serious deficiency diseases and are also transmittable to humans, though this does not often occur. Symptoms are very much the same as for round worms though rather more severe. The dog is usually thin with a ravenous appetite, and quite often has a depraved appetite which causes him to eat either his own or other dogs' excreta, also his breath is usually foul and he suffers from diarrhoea sometimes alternated with constipation. He is, in fact, an unhappy chap and must be treated with the least possible delay. The appropriate dose may be obtained from the Veterinary Surgeon or alternatively Sherley's Tape Worm Capsules are most effective and safe to use. One dose usually clears the dog completely within a few hours, and the absence of the segments thereafter from the motions is proof that the worms have been expelled.

All the foregoing pests and parasites are easily diagnosed and with a little care and trouble are also easily dispelled with the appropriate treatment. But if the treatment given does not put an end to constant scratching, then it may well be that a much more serious condition is present and the owner is advised to seek the help of the Veterinary Surgeon to make a diagnosis as he will have the knowledge and instruments to take a scraping from the dog's skin and to investigate this under the microscope. We will outline some of the more serious skin diseases.

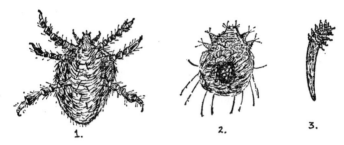

FIG. 11—Mites. (1) Harvest Mite, minute in size and resembling grains of red pepper. (2) Sarcoptic Mange mite. (3) Follicular Mange mite. All can be detected under a microscope, but too small to be seen by the naked eye.

COMMON MANGE (SARCOPTIC). The dog is continually biting and scratching himself and a rash of small red spots appear first round the eyes, on the elbows, the ankles and on the belly. This rash by degrees spreads over the whole of the body, and the irritation is so severe that it nearly sends him mad. It is extremely contagious from dog to dog and may also be picked up by humans. It is not too difficult to cure, and provided one really perseveres it can be completely eradicated in under a fortnight. The treatment usually consists of applying a strong lotion at intervals of three days, with germicidal baths in between. Sherley's Skin Cure is excellent combined with their Insecticidal Shampoo. Another excellent preparation for ridding the dog of all skin parasites is 'Seleen Suspension' prepared by Messrs. Abbotts of London. It is in the form of a wash, and if the instructions are carefully followed, the result is most satisfactory.

FIG. 12.—A cardboard collar fixed round the dog's neck which prevents him from scratching or rubbing his head, ears, eyes or muzzle.

FOLLICULAR MANGE. This form of mange is far more difficult to cure. It is thought that it may be a congenital disease, and dogs who suffer from it may be cursed with it all their lives and also in the case of bitches may infect their own puppies. It is nothing like so contagious as Sarcoptic mange. It is symptomatically different too, as it usually commences with several small bare patches on the face or muzzle. The bare patch is greyish in colour and looks rather like elephant skin and there are many little red weals or spots. As the disease progresses, the patches run into one another until the whole body may be affected with running sores. There is a very strong smell connected with this disease. It is a case which must have the attention of the Veterinary Surgeon, and the possibility of a course of vaccines might be helpful.

ECZEMA. Strictly speaking Eczema must not come under the heading of Pests and Parasites as it is really a blood condition manifesting itself through eruptions of the skin. It is not thought to be contagious, but is very often hereditary. It seems to attack the coarse-coated breeds more than those with a soft coat. Symptoms are constant licking and biting, and the usual parts affected are the root of the tail, the lips and round the eyes, flaps of ears and very often right inside the ear, and along the back. There are two types (1) Dry Eczema which produces a rough and scaly condition with patches of cracked skin, and (2) Wet Eczema where there are large inflamed areas which continually weep with serum. The best way to set about a cure is to look to the diet, and here a high meat diet is useful cutting out all or nearly all biscuits or cereals, or in fact anything starchy. Liver is good for the dog in these circumstances, rather underdone, as this will act as a laxative, but in addition Rhubarb Tablets (obtainable from Herb Royal Ltd. of Bridgwater, Somerset) are extremely helpful given in conjunction with Garlic and Leaf-Plasma tablets (from the same firm). Sherley's Eczema Lotion will help to clear the actual raw places on the dog. Frequent bathing will also benefit the dog. Again it must be stressed that in all cases of skin disease, or skin eruptions, it is absolutely essential that cleanliness should be the first consideration. Blankets must be washed regularly, bedding must be burned and renewed, baskets and boxes must be sprayed with strong disinfectant frequently. Unless these items are attended to, dogs will continue to re-infect themselves and other dogs, and thus any treatment that is given will be useless.

CHAPTER NINE

TONICS, APPETISERS AND INVALID FOODS

Vitamins – Value of Honey – Invalid Recipes

TONICS AND APPETISERS. The dog who is carefully fed and looked after should need few extra tonics or appetisers. Providing a dog has a balanced diet with plenty of variety comprising two-thirds meat, one-third biscuit, milk to drink, and bones to gnaw, he should do very well. He will also need hard running exercise and plenty of sunshine in the summer and warm draught free quarters in the winter. He should always have plenty of grass upon which to graze, as it is from this source that he gets his supply of Vitamin C. And of course, fresh clean water always available.

But after an illness or an accident necessitating restricted action, after rearing a family, or as a tonic if used at stud, or in the case of a puppy from four to nine months when he will have been teething and coping with the problems of 'growing up', it is often advisable to give a course of some tonic or conditioner, and the following are some which the Authors have found very useful for their own dogs.

Abidec: In droplet form, and as its name suggests, contains Vitamins A, B, C, D and E. An excellent tonic for building up dogs after illness, or after strain or stress.

Cytamen or Cytacon: The former is given by injection by the Veterinary Surgeon, and the latter is in liquid form for oral administration. It is an excellent tonic for the brood bitch mid-way through pregnancy, during the rather 'depressed' period, and again when she has finished feeding her babies and needs building up. Also excellent for those dogs who for no apparent reason are bad feeders or bad 'doers'. It always promotes a lively interest in food after only a few doses. Prepared by Glaxo.

Energol: A finely kibbled biscuit meal, but only one or two teaspoonsful should be given mixed in with the normal food. It provides many excellent vitamins, and in addition contains malt, bone meal, wheat germ, cheese protein, nuts and calcium. It is particularly useful for puppies while teething, and also helps to resist infection. Prepared by Sherley's.

Garlic Tablets: A most useful herbal tonic and internal cleanser. It is excellent for keeping worms away from the dog, and because of the cleansing properties will act as a disease resister. Prepared by several firms, particularly by Herb Royal Ltd. And also Sherley's prepared Creo-Garlic Tablets.

Halibut and Cod Liver Oil: Either in capsules or by drops. This is a tonic which is particularly useful in the winter time when there is little sun or grass. Contains vitamins A and D, and thus is an excellent means of resisting disease. All young dogs from eight weeks old will benefit from one of these oils during the winter. In summer, they are not necessary, since all the required vitamins are forthcoming from sun and grass. Indeed, in summer, both Halibut and Cold Liver Oil tend to over heat the dog a little.

Kenadex: A very good supplement to the feeding of puppies, as it supplies vitamins A and D. Prepared by Phillips Yeast Products.

Lactol Drops: Often owners like to give their dogs something in the way of tit-bits as reward for good behaviour. All too often pieces of chocolate, or biscuit, are given, neither of which do the dog anything but harm. Such things are bad for the teeth, cause tartar on the teeth, and tend towards obesity. But the Authors have found that Sherley's Lactol Drops are excellent tit-bits and most welcomed by their dogs. They contain Lactol and vitamins.

Lintox: An excellent disease resister, and also does much to build up strength after an illness, containing as it does, phosphates and minerals. Prepared by Sherley's.

Liver-Snaps: An excellent variation in biscuit, containing liver, wheat germ and bone meal. These should be given as a change once or twice a week. Manufactured by Sherley's.

Sherley-Vites: Excellent tablets which do much to get a dog back into fine condition after an illness or strain of some kind. These tablets contain vitamin B.12, and trace minerals, and are really first class. They act as a good appetiser for the choosey feeder, and after a very short time the appetite increases very noticeably. In this case, a two to three month course should be given in early Spring and again in Autumn. It will greatly increase virility, and will build up the stud dog carrying out a heavy stud programme.

Stress: Particularly recommended for the brood bitch, as this tonic will help to obviate deficiences of calcium during pregnancy, and while feeding the puppies. Prepared by Phillips Yeast Products.

Vetzymes: Most dog owners will be familiar with these excellent tablets which contain yeast and trace minerals. They seem to have special value when dogs are suffering from skin troubles and nervous affections. Prepared by Phillips Yeast Products.

Vitamin E. Succinate: This can be obtained from the Bioglan Laboratories either in tablet or powder form. It is particularly useful as a tonic for both stud dogs and brood bitches, for, as its name implies, it contains vitamin E, which is known as the 'fertility Vitamin'. A course of tablets for the brood bitch from a month before her expected heat, until her puppies have been weaned, will have a marked effect on fertility, milk production and general condition while rearing the babies. Equally the young stud dog will benefit from a course of Vitamin E given from ten months onwards.

INVALID FOODS. Feeding during illness and particularly feeding during convalescence, needs a lot of thought and care. The dog when really ill can eat very little, and everything offered must be bland and very easily digested. In convalescence, the great thing to aim at is getting as much nourishment, vitamins and minerals into the dog with the least amount of bulk and roughage. His appetite is bound to be somewhat erratic after illness, and therefore he must have food which tickles his palate. When dogs are really ill, one of the very best forms of nutrition is honey, and this can be given in plain cold boiled water, or else in warm milk. One cannot possibly give too much honey in illness, for it is particularly soothing to the membranes of the stomach, and most digestible as it has been pre-digested by the bees. Therefore we advocate honey in all drinks for the ill or convalescing dog. It is an advantage to use pure English honey and not the blended type.

A soup made from chicken, rabbit or sheep's head and brains, is usually acceptable, and can be poured over a little brown bread (never white bread).

An excellent milky drink which the Authors have used for years for many cases such as in illness, as a first food after an operation, as pre-whelping drinks, and first feeds after the puppies arrive and during lactation, and as a first class weaning food, is a mixture they have called 'The Casilan Mixture'. This is prepared as follows:

$$
\left.
\begin{array}{l}
\text{2 Parts Farex} \\
\text{1 Part Casilan} \\
\tfrac{1}{2} \text{ Part Glucodin}
\end{array}
\right\} \quad \text{All made by Glaxo}
$$

Mix the three powders together, then add enough really hot water to the consistency of *thick* cream. Beat up well, and then add sufficient cold milk to bring to the consistency of *thin* cream. In the case of a very ill dog, Casilan alone mixed with warm water until smooth and creamy, and given a teaspoonful at a time, is very beneficial as it is extremely bland and digestible, and as Casilan is ninety per cent protein it is very nourishing. 'Complan' is another very good base for a milky drink. Many dogs when seriously ill will take nothing but Sherley's Lactol, and if a certain amount of honey is added to the prepared drink, it is even more suitable for a really ill dog.

In the case of gastritis or frequent vomiting, a very excellent mixture is as follows:

> 1 *White* of an egg
> 1 Teaspoonful of glucose
> 1 Tablespoonful of cold boiled water

These should be well beaten together, and one teaspoonful given every hour. A few drops of brandy may be added. The white of the egg has the effect of soothing the linings of the stomach, and this usually stops the vomiting in a very short time.

For small Toy dogs, sometimes home-made sponge cake is useful. It is nourishing, and if a little dog has been ill and lost a lot of weight and needs fattening, a few small pieces of cake will work wonders. The following is a good recipe and easy to make:

> 2 eggs
> 4 ozs. castor sugar
> 4 ozs. margarine or butter
> 4 ozs. flour

Cream the butter and sugar, beat in the eggs, then fold in the flour and bake in a moderate oven for approximately twenty-five to thirty-five minutes.

For many dogs who are very seriously ill and very weak, Brands Essence of Chicken and also Essence of Beef are useful, as so little is needed to provide quite a deal of nourishment. Feed only a teaspoonful every hour.

Arrowroot is a good stand-by in cases of vomiting and diarrhoea. It is quite simple to make arrowroot gruel: Mix a heaped dessertspoonful with cold water until it is a thin, smooth paste. Boil half a pint of skimmed milk (i.e. with the cream taken off), and add the arrowroot to the milk. Stir well and cook for a few minutes. A dessertspoonful of honey should be added. When cool, a dog will usually relish this.

When the sick dog has recovered enough to be able to take solid food again, there is nothing better than good raw butcher's meat cut into pieces half an inch square. It is amazing how much energy will be noticed in the dog or puppy as soon as raw meat can be fed.

We can only end this consideration of invalid foods by repeating that honey and cold boiled water is the very safest thing to give a dog who is sickening for any severe illness, and also to any dog who is running a temperature. It is a natural food, and has tremendous healing properties, and until the Veterinary Surgeon has made or confirmed a diagnosis, honey and water is the only safe food or fluid that should be given as First Aid.

CHAPTER TEN

CARE OF THE OLD DOG

Comfort – Exercise – Feeding – Peace and Security

THERE COMES a time when one realises that one's beloved dog is ageing. One notices that perhaps he is not quite so anxious for a walk when the weather is cold or the ground wet; or that he takes a little while to get up in the morning; perhaps his hearing or his sight are not quite so sharp as they were; maybe he hesitates for a moment before starting to climb the stairs. One adds up his years and finds that he is well past his prime and is arriving at the age when he deserves quite a lot of extra care and comfort. Probably he sits rather closer to the fire in the Winter, and seeks out a patch of sun in the Spring and Summer and lies there rather longer, and he is not so anxious to chase the birds or be constantly on the move to investigate all the smells in the garden which always used to take his attention. When this situation arises, one must set one's mind to thinking how to make the declining years of the old dog as comfortable and happy as possible.

First of all, let us take his exercise. In the Winter he will probably appreciate a warm coat when the wind is chilly, a coat that is made of a soft and really warm blanket cloth, and which has a piece which covers his chest. If he is getting really old, then your pace must be adapted to his and he must not be expected to walk too fast or be made to run to catch up with you. On hot Summer days, he should have his walk in the cool of the early morning or else in the late afternoon. Do not expose him to rain or very wet grass as this will undoubtedly aggravate any tendency to rheumatism that he may have. Nearly all old dogs suffer more or less with pains in their bones and joints as they get old.

If he is not too anxious to get started in the morning allow him to take his own time over this, and don't insist that he rises early. Mild or severe deafness is a trial to old dogs, and often quite a trial to the owner too, but if the deafness is severe one must try to contact the old dog by signs and touch. It is amazing how quickly a dog will learn to know the meaning of sign language. It is not helpful continually to shout at an old dog, for although the loudest shout or word may get through to him, it may also fluster and frighten him. Just go up to him and gently touch him to attract his attention and then make signs to show him where he is to go or what he is to do. If on the other hand his sight is becoming bad, he may equally need to be touched to draw his attention to the fact that his dinner is ready, or the door is open for him to go out or come in. Always approach him from the front. Never touch him unexpectedly from behind, as this will make him jump and is bad for his heart. Steps and stairs often prove a difficulty, especially if with the advancing years your dog has put on a lot of extra weight. If there is a particularly steep step in the garden, put a little ramp there to help him.

There are certain things which become very important to the old dog. For instance, if he is very fond of his food, feeding time becomes the most important moment of the day and he will fret quite considerably if he is forgotten for any length of time and if his dinner is given to him much later than usual.

Sometimes his teeth are not in a very good state and he finds it difficult to eat. If this is so, his food should be soft and cut up into small pieces so that he does not have large, hard pieces to cope with. His basket or bed should be placed in a corner which is free from draughts and where it is really cosy. The bed must be large enough for him to lie out flat, for the old dog is stiff and cannot curl himself up in a ball. Don't move his bed from place to place—let him know that it is always to be found in the same place and where he expects it to be.

Sometimes the old dog may be unable to contain himself throughout the night – maybe he has drunk too much water or perhaps it is just old age. Don't scold him over this, as it will upset him so much and he simply cannot help it. A dog who has been clean all his life hates to make a mistake, and it is simply a matter of old age. Put a thick newspaper on the floor at night near his bed and he will undoubtedly use this if he has to, but never scold him.

The old dog seldom welcomes the bouncing high spirits of puppies or even of younger dogs. He may get very irritable if other younger dogs are around. So his bed must be put out of the way of the bouncing puppy or the teasing young dog. Also he may not welcome the exuberance of young children and may become a little snappy if they want to play with him when he only wishes to quietly doze off. It must be explained to children that he is getting old and must not on any account be teased or made to play when he is resting or in his bed.

But when everything has been done to make his old age quiet, comfortable and secure, there comes a time when one realises eventually that he is becoming a burden to himself. His aches and pains are constant, perhaps there is some disease which is slowly catching up on him, or perhaps he is becoming a little senile in his ways. He may lose his sense of direction and stand in the garden looking lost and not knowing which way to go or how to get back into the house. He may have a fear of being left alone and cry whenever you leave him. Then is the time when the decision has to be made that as his life is nearly at its end, one must take the step of having him put to sleep. Here again the words ' put to sleep ' must be taken literally, and you should do everything you can to make his passing simply a matter of ' going to sleep '. However painful to yourself, you owe it to your old pet to be with him at the end if you possibly can. At this time he needs the reassurance of your presence and must never be handed over to strangers for these last few minutes. Nowadays Veterinary Surgeons have the means of putting the old dog to sleep very swiftly and painlessly, but however much it saddens one, he must not be deserted at this time. A *very* strong sedative given two or three hours before the final injection is the kindest way. He will then be very sleepy and ' dopey ', and will have little instinct to know what is going to happen. The injection given by the Veterinary Surgeon will work speedily, and he will then drift swiftly away, not to wake again. However distasteful, upsetting or heartbreaking it is, one owes it to him to be there to hold and reassure him as long as he has need of one, and particularly at that last moment of his life.

In conclusion, the authors hope that this book will be of use to dog owners and breeders. To sum up, it must be stressed again that it is essential to know your dog from nose to tail when he is well, so that sudden symptoms of impending illness or disease may be recognised immediately. It is also essential to be prepared at all times to deal with emergencies, as it is at these moments that there is no time to ' read up ' the symptoms and treatment. Thus we suggest that Chapter V should be particularly well assimilated, and the Emergency First Aid Kit kept fully stocked and well labelled, so that immediate use may be made of it when sudden emergency arises.

APPENDIX A
TEMPERATURE CHART

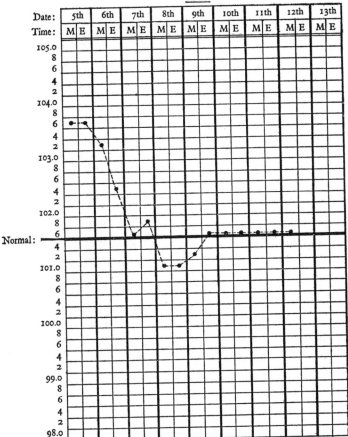

APRIL

Date:	5th	6th	7th	8th	9th	10th	11th	12th	13th

Symptoms: Lethargy, Diarrhoea, Vomiting on 5th April.
Temperature 103.6°.

Disease: Suspected Hepatitis.

Treatment: Veterinary Surgeon called 12 noon 5th April.
Arrived 2.30 p.m. and gave injection of Gamahtine.
Called again 6th April and gave another injection, called
7th April, 9th and 11th April. Complete recovery.

APPENDIX B

MEDICAL HISTORY SHEET

Name: PRINCE RODERICK OF SKYE. Date of birth: 4/8/60
Sire: Hamlet of Skye. K.C. Reg. No. 1234/61
Dam: Wendy of Skye. Stud Book No.: 0011/AN

Veterinary Treatment.

Bronchitis, Oct/Nov. 1961	500,000 I.U. Penicillin for five days. Complete recovery.
Fracture, right foreleg April 1962.	Ran a temperature for 3 days, then settled down. Plaster removed on 14/4/62. New one applied. Removed finally on 25/4/62. Leg completely mended.
Cough, January 1963	Suspected virus. Slight temperature. Injection of Gamahtine given. Temperature normal after two days. Dog isolated for 14 days, but it was false alarm.

Inoculations.

Epivak-Plus given 1st Novr. 1960.
Leptovak given on 15th Novr. 1960.
Booster inoculation given on 1st January, 1962.
Booster inoculation given on 1st January, 1963.

Notes:

First stud service on 12th September, 1961. Positive.
Second stud service on 14th January, 1962. Positive.
Third service on 20th February, 1962. From then on regular stud services.
Course of Vitamin E. Succinate given from 1/8/61 for six months.

WEIGHT CHART FOR SMALL KENNEL

Name of dog	RODDY	PRINCE	NINA	WENDY	Notes	Action taken
Normal Weight lbs.	12	15	14	15		
1st January 1961	12	15	16	14	Nina needs less. / Wendy needs more	Decrease meat 1 oz. and stop biscuit / Increase meat 1 oz and give egg daily
1st March 1961	12½	15	14½	14½	Nina nearly stabilised / Wendy improving	Continue present diet / Continue extras
1st July 1961	13½	15	14	15	Roddy needs less / Nina stabilised	Decrease biscuit / Normal diet
1st October 1961	12½	15	14	*18	Roddy stabilised / Nina stabilised / *Wendy in whelp	Remain on present diet / Remain on present diet / Remain on extra diet till puppies are 10 weeks old

Daily Normal Diet:

RODDY	7 oz. Meat	1½ oz. Biscuit	⅓ pt. Milk
PRINCE	10 oz. Meat	2 oz. Biscuit	½ pt. Milk
NINA	8 oz. Meat	1½ oz. Biscuit	⅓ pt. Milk
WENDY	10 oz. Meat	2 oz. Biscuit	⅓ pt. Milk

APPENDIX D

WHELPING RECORD

Name of Bitch: WENDY OF SKYE. Date of Birth: 12 January, 1958.

Due in Season	Actual Date	Mated	Due Whelp	Date Whelped	Result
(first season)	1/ 9/58	—	—	—	—
1/ 3/59	10/ 3/59	20/ 3/59	22/5/59	20/5/59	2 dogs 3 bitches
10/ 9/59	8/ 9/59	Rested	—	—	—
8/ 3/60	18/ 3/60	28/ 3/60	30/5/60	28/5/60	3 dogs 3 bitches
18/ 9/60	25/ 9/60	Rested	—	—	—
25/ 3/61	1/ 4/61	11/ 4/61	13/6/61	Missed	—
1/10/61	3/10/61	13/10/61	15/12/61	12/12/61	4 dogs 2 bitches
3/ 4/62	3/ 4/62	Rested	—	—	—

MATING RECORD

Date Mated:	Stud Dog:	Date Whelped	Result:
20/3/59	Leo of Skye	20/5/59	2d. 3b.
28/3/60	Leo of Skye	28/5/60	3d. 3b.
11/4/61	Captain of Skye	Missed	—
13/10/61	Leo of Skye	12/12/61	4d. 2b.

Notes: *1st Litter.* Much agitation for 24 hours prior to labour. Ran a temperature for three days after birth, then settled down. Fed pups till 6 weeks of age.

2nd Litter. No preliminary agitation, and whelped six puppies within 3 hours. Very calm and no temperature.

3rd Litter. A little agitated, and veterinary assistance required for first puppy. Other five arrived normally within four hours. No milk for first twelve hours, and pups were given Lactol twice. Temperature up a degree for two days. Fed pups till five weeks of age.

INDEX